PRISONERS OF WAR

PENELOPE GROGAN

By the same author:

The Mending of Cathlene
New Millennium 1995
ISBN 1 85845 008 X

The Catalysts and Other Poems
Vantage Press
ISBN 0 533 09219 1

PRISONERS OF WAR

BY

PENELOPE GROGAN

NEW MILLENNIUM

292 Kennington Road, London SE11 4LD.

Printed and bound by Arm Crown Ltd, Uxbridge Road, Middx.
Issued by New Millennium*
ISBN 1 85845 052 7
*An imprint of The Professional Authors' & Publishers' Association.

CHAPTER 1

"After what has happened, we shall have to move," my mother said, getting up. "We can't possibly go on living here." She then picked up Bristles and left the room.

My sister-in-law turned to me: "Why on earth," she asked, "does your mother always pick up the cat when she's upset?"

"In the circumstances it's surprising that she ever puts him down," I answered.

We were in the kitchen. My brothers' wives, Ann and Violet, were sitting at the table with cold, half-drunk cups of tea in front of them. They had been sitting there on and off for two years waiting for the war to end.

It was a bright winter day. The garden was covered with snow, and the branches of the yew tree that grew against the house cast moving shadows across the window panes and over the kitchen table where they sat.

Ann looked bored and slightly disagreeable. "Why doesn't your mother ever shut the door behind her?" She got up and shut it sharply and threw a log on the fire, scattering pieces of bark over the hearth.

"If the door is shut, I shan't be able to hear Johnie when he wakes up," Violet complained.

In the cold light you could see that Violet had been crying. She was obviously heavily pregnant, which was unfortunate because her husband, my brother David, had been a prisoner of war in the Far East for nearly two years. When her condition became known in the neighbourhood, the village people did everything in their power to humiliate and destroy her - they would have stoned her to death if they could!

My other brother Ian, Ann's husband, had been shot down on a bombing raid over Germany. He was in a prison camp there. My father died just before the outbreak of war, so we were a household of women (except for Johnie, who was only two). Our men were either dead or imprisoned far away. I suppose we too were prisoners all those years, not prisoners of the enemy like my brothers, but trapped by events and dread, where release and hope seemed ever remote and vague.

Violet looked up from staring at her cup.

"Hannah," she said, "would you be an angel and go up and see if Johnie is awake yet?"

I went upstairs - the bedroom was freezing cold. He was still sound asleep, his thumb in his mouth and holding tightly his shred of rag. He was surrounded by his own warm breathing and seemed to be in an aura of half-visible colours.

"Johnie," I whispered, "what is going to become of us all?"

CHAPTER 2

My father was a bacteriologist and had spent almost all his life in the Far East doing research into tropical diseases, particularly malaria. He was considerably older than my mother. They appeared inseparable, but I'm sure harboured mutual reservations. One thing that my mother did which infuriated Father was her constant habit of walking into a room and addressing him whilst he was reading either the newspaper or a book. He always closed the book sharply, or put the paper down with exasperation. Mother was always jealous of Father's obsession with his work. "His work always comes first," she said to me once. "I come a very poor second."

When he retired, we all came back to England and settled in London. Our house was a tall Kensington house on the Notting Hill Gate side of the Bayswater Road. It had five storeys, including a basement. On each landing were two high-ceilinged and spacious rooms, except on the top floor, where there was a jumble of servants' bedrooms and my father had his study. This was an uneasy room, with barred windows high up in the wall, so that you couldn't see out. I think it had been a nursery at one time. His room was entirely furnished with Chinese furniture, inlaid with mother-of-pearl, except for his desk.

On the wall behind where my father sat writing was a large framed photograph of a great friend. A friend he had shared rooms with at Cambridge. It showed a man muffled in Antarctic clothing standing in deep snow beside his pony. Both are touched here and there with frost. In winter, when it was getting dark, the picture hung in the evening shadows, only faintly lit by the desk lamp. This benign presence looked down in a ghostly way from the far-off snow where he had perished, reminding my father no doubt of the glowing years of his youth and the times they had spent together.

My brothers and I were sent to day schools. My father was not keen on the idea of boarding schools for his children; he wanted us to live and be together as a family, so I went to the local High School and my two brothers went, firstly, to prep-school, and then

3

to Westminster. Our lives at that time were terribly overshadowed by endless homework, partly I think because, having lived in the East, we had a lot of work to catch up.

In those days before the war, people had servants. In the London house we had four: a cook, a parlour maid, a housemaid and a rather superior lady who patched the sheets, mended pillowcases, did a little light dusting and took me to and from school daily. She never wore an overall or an apron like the others, but had a black silk dress and a little shining glass bead necklace round her neck. It lay on the bony weather-beaten motley top of her chest. Her hair looked as though it had come out of a mould, with not a hair out of place. She was called Mrs. Norton. Her hands also showed her superior status.

On our walks to school, she never talked about unsuitable things which the other servants were inclined to do, and she always tried to comfort me when I was in tears - which I'm afraid was quite often - as I didn't take easily to being imprisoned day after day, always trying to catch up with the others and get my work done.

My father was always uneasy about employing people and putting them in a basement to live below ground without natural light. We had an ever-changing staff (except for Mrs. Norton). Many of them were foreign girls who had come to learn English. They came in all shapes and sizes, and degrees of personal cleanliness.

CHAPTER 3

My mother's mother, Granny Bell, lived in a large rambling house. It stood below the South Downs in lush meadowlands.

My brothers and I spent all our school holidays there. Both my brothers were some years older than I was - I tagged along after them and they were wonderful to me.

The seasons were full of wild flowers and birds. Every year we looked forward to seeing the first swallow, and hearing the first cuckoo by 13th of April, which was Granny Bell's birthday. We spent nearly all of every day out of doors, whatever the weather, and when we came in, the meals that we ate were more delicious than any I have ever had since.

The most wonderful thing about Granny Bell was that she never expected or demanded affection of any sort, which made an atmosphere blissfully free from emotion.

She had grown rather shapeless over the years, her face wrinkled and her hands brown. I remember her in a battered old hat and faded dress, standing by the yew hedge, dreaming the gardeners' dream of achievement, which bears no relation whatever to reality, and the sight of the magnolias and the apple blossom scorched brown by late frosts; these had to be disregarded if morale was to be kept up and endeavour maintained.

She had six daughters, my mother's sisters. The Bells were a gifted family. Two of them, Kate and May, had been to the College of Music in London; Vanessa to Girton; Evelyn to the Birmingham School of Art; Mary to the Slade. Mary had made a very good marriage - as they say - to a rich landowner in Scotland. Her husband was called Douglas. They had four children, three boys and a girl - Alistair, Duncan, Andrew and Jean.

These were cousins of course but, as we spent more time there than they did, we looked upon them as intruders, treated them coldly and never showed them where the mushrooms were or the best blackberries.

Dreadful feuds broke out amongst the aunts from time to

time and, during the battles that took place, some of them shamelessly changed sides when they had been 'got at' by one of the others. Their husbands, the uncles, rarely joined in the squabbles, but amongst themselves they didn't get on very well either. Granny Bell seemed completely oblivious to all this family rowing and wandered about her garden, secateurs in hand, snipping here and there.

One of the uncles, James, the husband of the clever Vanessa and father of Susan and Peter, we dreaded because he made teasing jokes which we didn't understand. He had the reputation of loving children, and pinched my cheeks and chucked me under the chin. He even upset Granny Bell's dogs, Bessie and Buster. You could see how embarrassed they were by his unwanted advances - they hung their heads and looked away sideways out of the corner of their eyes. In spite of this he had to be tolerated, even encouraged, because he gave us money at Christmas. When we were little he used to give us a new half-crown each, but he had increased the amount year by year, until in 1937 it had become a pound. This was a huge sum of money - it paid for nearly all the Christmas presents that we had to buy.

In the fraught atmosphere that often developed at the family gatherings, sentences, half-whispered, could often be heard behind doors (if you held your breath to listen). "Tony's getting worse, don't you think?" "Wasn't he rude at lunch?" "Someone should tell Evelyn about her hair, it's got so dreadfully thin on top - she doesn't seem to know. Why on earth doesn't Fred tell her?"

But when we were alone with Granny, Marchfold came into its own. Fresh air blew in at the open doors and the sun seemed to shine in all the rooms.

My grandfather had been dead for a very long time. I do really believe that he had been almost entirely forgotten. I only heard Granny mention him on one occasion, and that was as 'the girls' father'. I once asked her what he had done in his life and she replied, "not much." There was, however, a photograph of a very young man on her dressing table, behind other pictures of grandchildren. He had a startled old-fashioned look, like a favourite rather stupid dog - I never asked who it was. There were a pair of unclaimed boots in the cloakroom which may have been his and some fishing tackle.

The aunts often talked about living in Egypt, and reminded one another of the garden in Rome and events in other places, so I had supposed that they had lived abroad when they were children, and concluded that my grandfather must have done something that took his family overseas.

There were two cousins who stood out from the rest: one was Kate's child, Sylvia, who was known by the unfortunate nickname of 'Silly'. She had long blonde hair and delicate features and a flawless complexion. She was also a paragon of virtue, always ready to help; unselfish and thoughtful and never rude. She was always being held up to us as a template from which we should copy our lives. The other was Harry, the child of May. He was immensely clever. He won scholarships and school prizes and was destined to be head boy. Just the look of him made my brothers sulk. As a matter of fact, he never was made head boy after all. Why, we never found out.

At Marchfold there were two very old maids. They had lived and worked there nearly all their lives, the only servants left of the complete household staff who had once been resident there.

Ellen did the cooking and Ivy was the parlour housemaid. Other young women used to come in from the village to clean from time to time and to help when the house was full.

I couldn't believe that anybody could be so old-looking as Ellen and still be alive. She baked delicious little cakes for us to eat between meals. I used to run into the huge old kitchen which was in the oldest part of the house and say, "Ellen, I've come for a cake." She was very deaf, but she knew why I was there without hearing and would shuffle off and get the cake tin.

There was one other retainer - Tom Norton. Small and bowlegged, he had started life as a groom before he took to gardening. He had been one of many gardeners once, but now he was the last and only gardener, and if asked where he worked, he always replied, "'Ead gardener at Marchfold." He lived in the cottage by the gate at the end of the drive with his rather sour wife, Joan.

7

It was undeclared war between him and Granny Bell. She thought him stupid, but knew that he had a shrewd peasant cunning - she knew too that he pilfered the vegetables and fruit from the kitchen garden. He gave away produce to gain popularity in the village, where he was a church warden, and even occasionally actually sold some to friends who owned small shops in the neighbourhood. He got round this by saying to Granny, "It seemed a pity to waste the beans. I let Alf have some." Or, "I knew you didn't want all them marrows." In fact, he was as awful as he dared to be without risking getting the sack and having to leave. In turn, Granny curbed her tongue because he mowed the lawn and cut the yew hedges. The little garden outside his cottage was always a blaze of colour in summer, with all the flowers that Granny hated most - bedding-out plants and, later, dahlias.

Granny always addressed him as 'Norton', after the custom of the time, and he usually spoke of her as 'she' and 'er', as in "I told her, but she wouldn't listen." We children thoroughly enjoyed baiting him and spent many happy hours stalking him in the kitchen garden and making things awkward. He tried to win my brothers over to his side, but without success.

Every Sunday, Granny, Ellen and Ivy walked to church together. It was rather slow progress because of Ellen. The path went across two fields and over a wooden bridge that crossed the river to the churchyard. If the weather was bad, Granny drove dangerously by road in her little old car. In other times, she had had a driver and a bigger car and a fur rug, which now lay folded up on the box in the cloakroom.

Granny never made us go to church, but occasionally we did. My brothers usually bicycled, but I walked with the others. For some reason I remember one time vividly; it was early summer and the fields were yellow with buttercups which soon dusted my polished shoes with pollen. It was hot, but inside the church it was cold. There was a bluebottle buzzing against a stained glass window. Mrs. Morris said her prayers in spitty whispers. She was wearing self-righteous white gloves - they looked like little cats' paws.

The organ played (you could hear its pumping action); Ivy

sang loud and out-of-tune and Ellen had to be hoisted off her knees after all the prayers. When Tom Norton came round with the collection bag, he thrust it in front of Granny in the most aggressive way. She told me that when he did that, she always closed her eyes and said to herself, "We are all equal in the eyes of the Lord ... except Norton!"

When my brother David complained about Mr. Jeffries' long sermons, Granny said, "I know they're hopeless - they have no proper beginning or middle, but I always remind myself that there is going to be an end. At least they aren't out of a book and they must be his own work. I'd know a Jeffries' original anytime, and he is quite a nice man, so I suppose we should think ourselves lucky."

Mr. Jeffries often ended his piece with the remark, "I only hope that I've given you something to think about as you leave the church."

Later on in that year we had all gone to the 11 o'clock service and taken our places in the pew by the pillar. After kneeling down for a brief prayer, as we had been taught and reaching for our hymn books, we saw that on the altar were some very fine lillies. Granny thought that she recognised them. As the service progressed she got more and more obsessed with the idea that they had come from her garden. She tried in vain to banish these agitated thoughts from her mind. They interfered with her devotions, but the more she tried, the more they intruded.

When we got home she went straight down to the rose garden, where the lillies grew in a great clump against the wall. To her relief they still stood, as tall and beautiful as ever. She was immediately ashamed of herself and her suspicions, and said how unfair she had been in accusing poor Norton of stealing her lillies and added, "perhaps I'm getting old and silly." However, on getting nearer the lillies and having a closer look, she found that every other one had indeed been picked. Immediately she felt triumphant and freed from her guilt, but furious with Norton for helping himself and making her frightened of being old.

It later came out that the wretched man had cut them to give to Daisy Wilks, whose turn it was to do the church flowers. In spite

9

of his advanced years, there had been rumours circulating about him and Daisy.

"It's outrageous," Granny said. "I can't put up with it any longer. He'll have to go." But she did put up with it and he didn't go.

CHAPTER 4

We slept on the very top floor of Marchfold, where a number of small rooms gave on to a long, low gallery-like attic with arched beams. It was a magical place to be, to have wild, rough games and to do as we liked. My brothers even played football up there. If you looked out of the small dormer windows over the parapet, you could see the whole garden far below, but my father got a bee in his bonnet about the dangers of fire and, after a discussion with Granny, we were brought down to sleep on the first floor, in more spacious and less interesting rooms where we were under the surveillance and restraint of our elders. We had never had to fold our night things when we were up in the attic, but once lower down, we had to turn down our beds and leave everything tidy and put away.

My father was working at the Colonial Office at that time and he and my mother could only get down to the country at weekends. Their arrival put further restrictions on us. Although my father seldom said anything, we knew what high standards of behaviour he expected from us.

Of course, we had various mishaps as we grew up. My brother Ian fell out of a tree and had concussion. Dr. McClean was sent for; he came bringing with him some special cuttings for Granny - he too was a keen gardener. Ian was put to bed in a darkened room, but next day he took a turn for the worse. His temperature soared and he was delirious. It was very frightening. My mother and father came rushing down from London. They sat by his bed all night. By morning, however, he was red and swollen with spots. Although he was very ill, it was a relief to know that it was only the measles.

When we weren't well, Granny never took much notice. As far as I can remember, we were never brought anything to eat in bed. "If you're well enough to eat, I suppose you are well enough to come down and get it," she remarked on one occasion.

You would be lucky if she looked round the bedroom door when she came in from the garden at lunchtime and asked if you felt better, and if she did the same at night just before she went to bed.

At home, when we were ill in bed, my mother provided us with lovely things to do or read, and if we were too unwell to do anything, both our parents read to us endlessly. It was lovely to be made such a fuss of, but not of course for too long.

Granny only went away from Marchfold twice a year. In the spring she went to stay with her only remaining sister, Pamela, who lived in Yorkshire. In the autumn she went to London to stay a few days at her club, and whilst there she did a little shopping and saw her friends. The few friends that were still alive. I believe they gathered from the distant countryside to gossip and to go once, or even twice, to the theatre. They went to jolly untroubled musical shows - I seem to remember one was called 'Mr. Cinders'.

While Granny was on her yearly London visit, she never failed to take time to come and see us at home. She came by taxi. Away from her familiar surroundings, she looked a completely different person. Dressed in her out-of-London clothes, she appeared very vulnerable. With her face painted and her hair done, she looked almost freakish. I felt guilty and embarrassed looking at her. She never wore make-up in the country and, anyway, she was very wrinkled and old.

In our turn, Mother and I always went to see her at her club in Cavendish Square. We sat with her in the huge elegantly furnished drawing room and looked through the long windows down onto the small, grimy, paved, classical garden below with its sooty urns and struggling ivy; little parlour maids quietly brought trays of tea and toast and little cakes; the chandeliers lit the room faintly in the settling London afternoon gloom; everyone kept their voices down, and in the hush I was afraid the other groups of ladies would hear me swallowing my tea: the more I tried to suppress the noise, the louder it sounded. Granny always ate a hearty tea and, on one occasion, sent for more buttered toast three times.

When we were leaving she often whispered, "I can't wait to get home to see the dogs and grub in the garden."

CHAPTER 5

My father's only brother had been killed in the First World War, but he still had a half-sister. Her name was Ruth and she was short and stout with little feet. There was nothing interesting about her whatsoever, except perhaps her strange tottering walk, which the ladies of the French Court affected, I believe, during the reign of Louis XIV. It gave her a certain gliding elegance which she would otherwise have lacked. My father found her (and I exaggerate only a little) unbearable and, sad to say, we found her the same. He was fond of her as well, which made him feel guilty. She had a great respect for him, as she had for her husband, Arthur, who was a don at Oxford, whose academic status and brilliance was legendary. They had no children, so her life was dedicated to all his terrestrial needs, from producing his spectacles at the right moment, to typing whatever he wrote. She spoke of him in gasping breaths, as though it was almost sacrilege to say his name aloud. She fed him the food that he liked, but mostly food she thought would be good for him, and stopped him falling over. When I, myself, dared to speak to him, I always felt that I was wasting his time.

He gave the impression that he couldn't bother to listen to what I had to say or, indeed, to what anyone had to say. Sometimes he made some mundane remark himself, like, "There now, I've forgotten the Listerine," or "Ruth, did you remember to lock the back door?" Otherwise he remained mostly silent in our presence. Whether he ever conversed with people who he considered to be his intellectual equals, I don't know. I imagine that he did.

Ruth and Arthur shared a common passion: an intense love of opera. For this reason they came often to stay with us; fortunately, seldom for more than one or two nights at a time. They came for performances at Covent Garden and, latterly, to Glyndebourne. They stopped with us then and on their way to and from Germany. When they could, they made the pilgrimage either to Munich or Bayreuth - the sacred places where the Wagner Festivals were held alternatively. I think Bayreuth had the edge on Munich for them - it

13

had perhaps more intimate connections with King Ludwig and the revered composer and was therefore a holier shrine.

My father said that there were only three sorts of people in the world: those who loved opera, those who hated it, and the lucky majority who had never even heard of it.

Ruth and Arthur, I remember, were nearly always dressed in countrified tweeds, smelling slightly of mothballs, but their opera-going clothes were different. Arthur became more significant-looking and elegant, and Ruth was transformed into a regal figure, dressed in purple and red velvet. For Germany she had massive thin floating garments because of the intense late summer heat in South Germany - the time that the Wagner Festivals were held.

At the Bayreuth Opera House, it was often stifling by night and you were locked into the wooden building, act by act, with no escape whatever, not even if you fainted or fell dead. Such was the ferocious devotion of the faithful. My father was appalled when he heard that the audience was imprisoned during performances: "the fire risk," he said, "is horrifying." My mother remarked that "if Ruth and Arthur wished to be burnt up like chops it was their affair." "And anyway," she added, "I'm sure they could think of no better way to die than be consumed by Brunnhilde's guarding flames and their ashes carried aloft by a blast from the wind instruments."

Over those pre-war years, Ruth and Arthur were such frequent visitors that our spare-room became known as 'Ruth and Arthur's room'. The extraordinary thing was that they never invited us to Oxford. Never did they once ask the boys down to see the colleges or take us round the college gardens, or even give us a meal.

On one occasion when we called on them on our way back from visiting the Cotswolds, we didn't get much of a welcome. Great play was made of the fact that they were too busy for words. They gave us horribly strong Indian tea and some mixed biscuits out of a tin, and we had to continue our journey home annoyed and with indigestion.

The family called my father Bill or William, but Ruth called him Billiam, to our intense frustration. She called him Billiam in her

14

strident voice that jarred the house and struck the air. When my father heard her arrive, he used to say, "Oh no!", and shut himself in the lavatory, which was a stupid thing to do because sooner or later he had to come out, but not before he heard her shout, "Where is Billiam?"

CHAPTER 6

My brother David went up to Cambridge in 1935. The house felt very empty without him. Ian went two years later.

At that time our house in London was full of Westminster School friends, especially in the summer. They used to come on Sundays to play tennis in the square. We had huge teas afterwards in our bit of garden and in the schoolroom: strawberries and cream, bread and jam and mountains of buns.

That year my hero, Lawrence of Arabia, crashed on his motorbike and was killed, and it was the King's Silver Jubilee. Hitler had been in power for two years; Germany was re-arming on a massive scale and the persecution of the Jews had begun in earnest; Stalin was in Moscow; the Italians invaded Abyssinia; Spain was in turmoil - there were wars and rumours of wars. The East was restless and India rebellious. The world was erupting all around us - I thought it was very exciting.

"Your father is very worried," my mother said. "I only hope it doesn't make him ill."

CHAPTER 7

The sun was still shining on the houses across the street and golden reflected light filled the dining-room where we were having our evening meal. Neither of the boys was present, but Ruth and Arthur were with us. The windows were open. Our stray cat, Bristles, sat on the parapet at the top of the basement steps watching the passers-by. Because of the long, dry summer the leaves were falling one by one from the two pollarded lime trees that grew in front of the house. There were hardly any cars in those days. A sadly sluttish Estonian girl called Erna was waiting at table - when she lent over to clear away the plates, you could smell her sweat, and her greasy hair fell across her face.

Our guests were on their way to Salzburg to stay with some old friends - a Jewish professor and his wife, who shared their interest in music. On their way home after the visit, they were going to spend a few days in the Black Forest, a favourite spot of theirs, in the hills above Freiburg.

Ruth was sipping her soup from spoon in a contrived way, avoiding with difficulty her big bosom. Arthur had changed his spectacles twice and had spilt some soup on the table-mat.

"We're looking forward very much to seeing the Laubentals again, and Salzburg is such a beautiful town," Ruth remarked, "and, of course, Austria has always been one of the loves of my life. The saddest thing though is the unemployment and poverty there since the war."

"Aren't your friends in Salzburg very disturbed by the threat that Austria may be taken over by the Germans?" my father asked.

"Oh yes," Ruth answered. "Indeed they are, but I keep telling them that they have nothing to fear. Hitler has achieved such miracles in Germany, I can't see why he shouldn't do the same for Austria. Germany has been rescued from utter despair and brought back to life, the value of their currency restored and confidence has returned. You should see the young people, they are so full of purpose, marching along singing, and not with guns as people infer, but carrying spades over their shoulders. You should go to Germany, Billiam, and see for yourself."

"What about the Jews?" my father persisted.

"What indeed?" Ruth declared. "What indeed! They are to be seen everywhere, busy about their daily business and going into their synagogues. All this talk about persecution is just Communist propaganda. Anyway, the trouble with the Jews is that they don't like events taken out of their hands. If only they would be content to share power, I'm sure a lot of their immediate difficulties would be resolved."

Arthur looked up from his soup. "Will," he said, looking at my father, "I do admire the Chinese furniture that you've got in the spare room. One day, I imagine, it will probably be quite valuable and, even if not valuable, it is so delightfully pleasing. It was clever of you to bring it home."

We all listened very attentively to what he said, and because he hardly ever spoke, we expected it to be something profound.

After the soup came lamb chops. Silence was broken as the conversation turned again to Germany and the Germans.

"I think it's more than likely that the Germans may save the world - no one else is standing up to Communism. If Germany is re-arming, which is doubtful, it's because of this menace, threatening to undermine civilization. I suppose you could say that Russia is at war with us already."

"Don't say that Ruth," said my mother, "it sounds so frightening."

"And another thing," Ruth continued, delicately chasing a chop bone across her plate, "the young people in Germany look so healthy and happy. When we were last in Tittersee, we were taken to see a Hitler youth hostel. It was a long, low chalet-style building, full of light and air and polished floors. They showed us their cupboard: the clothes on the hangars had to be an inch and a half apart, exactly. It's a trivial thing in itself, but discipline and direction are so good for an ordered life. Young people like to be told what to do, for their own sakes. Look at the same generation here, an untidy lot they are, lounging around. I was reading only a little while back about the Debating Society at Westminster - a motion was proposed 'That we will not fight for King or Country' and the motion was actually carried. I trust Ian was not involved."

"I'm afraid he was," my father told her.

"What a disgrace. Aren't you ashamed of him? If he were my boy, I'd be too ashamed to admit it."

"He's not your boy," my mother snapped, and an uneasy silence fell on us.

Erna cleared the table and brought the pudding. It was summer fruit pudding, made of raspberries. It was a beautiful deep red and juice had oozed out on to the dish round it. Erna had forgotten to bring the sugar and cream. My mother asked me to ring the bell.

"The sugar and cream, Erna, please," my mother asked, when she appeared.

Erna went down to the kitchen again. We sat waiting and, after hearing raised voices from below, there came the most dreadful piercing screams. We all rose from our chairs and froze half standing with shock, the slices of abandoned raspberry pudding in front of us. The screams continued. My father left the table and ran down to the basement. He was followed by my mother. "Stay where you are," she said to me.

My father came up and telephoned for an ambulance. Erna was carried out on a stretcher and driven away, her screams mingling with the urgent sound of the ambulance bell.

We were all white and trembling, only Arthur seeming totally unmoved. He ate his pudding without sugar or cream and didn't even seem curious about the screams.

It later transpired what had happened. Erna had gone back to the kitchen to fetch the cream. It was in a little silver jug on the kitchen table. Accidentally she knocked it over and the cream spilt on to the freshly scrubbed top. Irish Kitty, our cook, had just cleaned it. It was her pride. When she saw what had happened, she flew into a passionate rage and threw the kettle which she had in her hand at Erna. Unfortunately, the kettle was full of boiling water.

Ruth said, "I suppose you'll have to sack this mad Kitty person. A pity though, because she's quite a good cook."

21

Erna's injuries miraculously turned out to be very superficial and she was soon back from hospital, with hardly a mark to be seen. There followed tears and reconciliations, but it was no good, because, understandably, she felt afraid of Kitty.

After this upset, Bristles disappeared. Three days later he turned up again. Instead, however, of going back to his kitchen home, he adopted a chair in the schoolroom and made it his permanent place, and my mother his convenient person. That was how Bristles came to be my mother's cat.

CHAPTER 8

As well as Ruth and Arthur's visits, the Bell aunts used to come and stay with us. But it was always for a reason, like seeing a doctor or taking one of their children to see a special dentist, having tonsils out or going to the sales. They were easy and comfortable guests on the whole; one at a time they were easy to cope with.

The sister that my mother had been closest to in childhood was Mary. She was the one who had married the handsome rich heir to an estate in the Highlands. He was the eldest son of an ancient Scottish family. In the early days of their marriage, some of the sisters had been to Scotland to see her and she had spent one Christmas at Marchford, but she gradually distanced herself, and never came to any of the gatherings, either in Sussex or elsewhere. This was considered to be because she thought herself too grand and moved in different circles. "She doesn't want to be bothered with us now," they said. "After all, we are a fairly rough lot I suppose, and we don't know ANYBODY."

Sometimes we got to hear that she had been in London, but she never came to see us. Everybody was permanently offended with her. Alistair and Andrew, her sons, were already at Eton. "She comes down to see them all right," they commented. "I bet it's not him, it's her. He's not the snob." Granny Bell had never even seen Jeanie, Mary's only daughter.

The years went by ...

We were sitting in the schoolroom having tea. Ian had just got back from school and was eating vast quantities of bread and jam. My mother was putting hot water in the tea pot. Bristles was sitting on his chair, his eyes squeezed tightly closed with pleasure. My father came in with the evening paper, lent over and kissed my mother. My fingers were sticky and I had finished all my homework. Everything seemed so settled, so pleasant and so perfectly all right. We were all in our right places at the right time. It was warm by the gas fire and there was a smell of bread. "It is difficult," my father always said, "to remember that we are living on a thin layer between molten rock and freezing space."

The telephone rang. My father went to answer it. He came back.

"Marion," he said, "it's Mary."

"Mary?" my mother repeated. "Mary who?"

"Your Mary - your sister."

"What on earth does she want?" my mother said, getting up and going to the telephone.

When she returned to the schoolroom she was obviously upset and shaken.

"Mary has begged me to go to Scotland at once. I'll go and pack my things and go on the night sleeper."

My father and I put her on the train. As far as I can remember, it was the first time she had ever been away without us. It felt very peculiar. As we left her she called out, "I'll telephone as soon as I get there and tell you what the trouble is."

She rang up at lunchtime the next day. Her voice was faint and far away.

"Here I am," she said, "safely arrived. I can't say anything at the moment. I'll try and write. I shall probably be bringing Mary and Jeanie back with me in a few days time, but I don't know yet when."

A letter did come. My mother always called my father 'Man'. The letter said:-

'Man,
I will tell you all about it when I get home. We will travel to London next Thursday (five days time).
Love to everybody,
M.'

I had only seen Aunt Mary once before and that was at Marchfold. She had the reputation of being the beauty in the family and earlier photographs that I had seen certainly bore that out. She looked tall and willowy. When she arrived I was horrified to see that her face was badly bruised and she had her arm in a sling. She wore a scarf over her head, which partly hid her face.

My eight-year-old cousin, Jeanie, who I had never seen before was holding her mother's hand. She was so pale and fair that she looked like a little moth. Her eyes were cast down and you could see her long, almost white eye lashes.

Mary stayed for almost a fortnight, but my mother still wouldn't tell us what had happened. Ian and I were dying of curiosity. I suppose she must have told my father.

While they were with us, Aunt Mary sat in the schoolroom. She just sat there, only getting up for meals or to go to the downstairs cloakroom or to go to bed. She never even looked at the paper. She never walked into the garden or took Jeanie out.

While I was at school, Jeanie occupied herself almost endlessly with the contents of our old toy cupboard. She found a doll of mine that I had called Laura, with one eye rolled back to front. In the basement, we unearthed a fairy cycle and a dolls' pram. I taught her to ride the bicycle in the square. My mother and I took her to the Round Pond in Kensington Gardens to feed the ducks and watch the model boats. We took her to the Serpentine and to see the carving of Peter Pan on the tree stump. She hardly said anything, but once asked me, "Does your Daddy ever get cross?" Although she had three big brothers, she was very shy of Ian.

I sensed that Aunt Mary found our household both shabby and dull. Being with us didn't suit her at all. By the end of the two weeks, the bruising on her face had almost gone.

When they left to go home, Jeanie hung back in the hall and silently started to cry and ran to my mother, but as inevitable arrangements were carried out, she was quickly and forcibly put into the taxi.

After they had gone, I heard at last what it was all about. After arriving in Scotland, my poor mother had one shock after another. She learnt for the first time that the handsome, rich, refined Douglas was subject to terrible bouts of drinking. Not long after her wedding, Mary realized that her husband was an incurable drunk. At first she tried to cover it up, but as time went on, and he got steadily worse, it became more and more difficult. As she didn't want the family to know, she withdrew from all contact with them. For the first years she never spoke of it aloud; it was so shameful and embarrassing. Just as she had withdrawn from the family, so their friends and neighbours drew back from them. She and her children clung together as though they were at sea on a raft.

In all the years Douglas had never been physically violent, only cruelly abusive, but this time it had been different. Fortunately the boys, Alistair, Andrew and Duncan were away at school. Douglas had followed Mary and Jeanie upstairs and set about Mary, repeatedly hitting her, shouting and raging. They got away from him and locked themselves in a bedroom, where for sometime he had remained kicking and banging at the door. At last two burly retainers, who had heard terrible noises from far off, came and dragged their master away. It was the next day that Mary had called my mother to her side.

Douglas took himself off - no one knew where. Of course, he came back before long. Whether things were in any way improved when Mary got back, we never heard.

CHAPTER 9

Arthur had not been very well: Ruth decided that he needed a change, so she arranged for them to go to the Black Forest for two weeks.

"It will be beautiful at this time of year. We have never seen it under snow before and we can take walks amongst the pine trees and breathe the good air," she said.

They set off for Germany with a great mountain of luggage, heavy with books.

Several weeks went by ...

"It must be almost time for Ruth and Arthur to be back," my father said, mildly dreading their return, but we heard nothing.

"I expect," my mother commented, "they've decided to stay longer because it's so nice."

Then a letter came from Arthur. It described how, on one of their gentle walks in the forest, Ruth had slipped on an icy patch and fallen heavily on a large lump of snow, breaking her leg in two places. Poor Arthur had to leave her lying in the snow like a wounded animal and go to get help.

I imagined her lying there, listening to his footsteps receding into the distance: the lonely silence only broken by the sound of the wind in the trees, and the occasional thud of snow falling off the branches, as it did in the woods at Marchfold.

The accident happened early in the day, at about 10 o'clock. She was eventually taken down to Freiburg by ambulance. As there had been a fresh fall of snow, the roads were very treacherous. They had to travel with great caution and go very slowly, partly because Ruth was in considerable pain. They didn't get to the hospital till after midnight.

Since then she had undergone a painful operation. Her shin bone had been wired together. She now lay in the Scherogischer Private Clinic, which was attached to a huge new state hospital, built in the fields just beyond the workers' flats on the outskirts of Freiburg. Poor Arthur begged my father to come out to Germany and see if he thought Ruth was having the best treatment. He, himself, was staying at a hotel opposite the railway station. Every day he went by tram to the end of the tramlines and then walked the last mile to the hospital, where he spent the long day with Ruth. He said it was bitterly cold, with a piercing wind. Most days it snowed or sleeted and the roads were often a foot deep in slush, which then froze. He went on to say that one of the worst things was the food at the hospital. 'There is not much fruit to be had, and I spend a lot of time going from one shop to another trying to find oranges for Ruth. She likes the juice. They say that the vitamin C in it will help to knit her leg together.'

My father didn't really want to go to Germany. He tried to persuade himself that he couldn't do anything to help even if he did. Ruth and he had never been very close anyway. He tried to convince himself, without success, that interfering might do more harm than good. In the end he knew he should go. Everything that he had heard or read about the Nazi regime filled him with horror and made his decision to go harder. My mother then insisted on going with him.

"I can't possibly allow you to go on your own," she said. I begged to be allowed to go as well.

"You can't possibly miss school," she retorted, but she and my father gave in. The next day, we took the train to Harwich and sailed on the night crossing to the Hook of Holland.

In the morning I looked out of the porthole of my cabin and saw, to my amazement, a Dutchman dressed in baggy trousers and clogs, just as you saw them in pictures or on tea-cosies. There was a keen sea breeze as we left the ship and boarded the train. The winter countryside of the continent whizzed past us, hour by hour, until the light faded and the windows became black and mirror-like.

That night we were sitting in a stuffy, plush-covered dining room at the Bahnhof Hotel in Freiburg. The whole place reeked of past opulence, now sadly moth-eaten and shabby. The tassels that hung about the place were mostly coming unravelled, and the carpet was threadbare. The trains coming into the station and drawing out, and the endless clanging of passing trams rattling in the street, created the whole background. In the hotel hung a picture of the Führer with his smarmed-sideways hair, joke moustache and hypnotic, staring eyes.

We had just started our evening meal, when Arthur arrived back from the hospital. He seemed worn and lost. Having never made conversation with us before, it was very difficult. The atmosphere was oppressive and disastrous. The other diners in the room were very subdued, spoke in low voices and regarded us with ominous suspicion. I was afraid they might think that my father was Jewish because of his hooked nose. One of the waiters was openly hostile and rude.

Arthur thanked my father for coming, after a fashion, but was obviously surprised and slightly put out by seeing my mother and me.

"I thought you would have come on your own," he remarked rather peevishly, adding, "I don't think Ruth will want too many visitors."

The food we had eaten was heavy and dull and we all went to bed cross. I wished I had never come. I'm sure my father was wondering how soon we could get away.

Next day we went with Arthur to the hospital. Instead of snowing, it was raining, freezing rain. We went by taxi. As he had said, the private wing of the hospital lay a little apart from the main building, which was gigantic, with many blocks housing different medical and surgical departments. Inside the private ward it was warm and spacious with huge glass windows. There were black leather armchairs grouped under tall indoor plants in the hall. The floor shone with polish. All the rooms had double doors to ensure silence. Nuns, who did all the nursing, moved about silently in their felt slippers. They were dressed in bright blue habits with huge, white, winged headdresses.

Arthur led us to Ruth's room. There she was, her large body, released from its customary control, lying round her almost like a heap of frogspawn. There was a cradle over her leg, under the bedclothes. She was reading.

"Hello Billiam!" she said, looking over her glasses. "How

29

extremely good of you to come. Quite unnecessary, I feel, but Arthur has been so worried. I'm sure when you have talked to Professor Reine you will be able to reassure him. After all, he is one of the foremost surgeons in Germany. I understand that people come to him from all over the world. I couldn't really have broken my leg in a better place. I'm afraid he says I shan't be able to leave here for another five or six weeks, anyway, not until the wire has been removed. It's been remarkably painful, but I'm told my legs will be the same length."

Two nuns came in: a short one with a wrinkled face and square hands and a young one, serene and beautiful, like a Botticelli. Ruth introduced them to us. Fortunately, Ruth spoke fluent German. The nuns asked us to leave the room for a few moments while they attended to their patient.

While we sat outside waiting, a boy on crutches came by with his leg in plaster. With him was his mother. My father got into conversation with them, as he did with everyone, to my acute embarrassment. They turned out to be White Russians exiled in France since the Revolution. The boy's father, a Count, had been a taxi driver in Paris now for many years, but a better-off relation of theirs, knowing that they had never had the chance of a holiday, had paid for them (the mother and son) to go to the Black Forest to ski. No sooner had they arrived, than the boy fell and broke his leg on the slopes of the Feld Berg. It was a terrible blow. The mother told us that at weekends when the ski runs were very crowded, thirty or forty casualties were brought in to the hospital, many of them serious. The last week, she said, a poor woman was carried in - she had bent down to adjust the laces on her boot just as a skier came down the slope at a great pace and the points of his skis had gone into her face.

We went into Ruth's room, and sat aimlessly looking out through the sliding glass door at the terrace and a rough grass field, beyond which was the city of Freiburg and the hills. Arthur had bought a juice squeezer and was squeezing oranges in a frenzied kind of way, spilling juice and dropping oranges and getting the whole operation mixed up with his handkerchief.

CHAPTER 10

A day later, my father went to see the Professor. He was a huge, blonde, savage-looking Viking of a man, well over six foot tall. He was dressed in Nazi uniform; as he came forward to shake hands, he explained and excused his dress by saying that every three months, all doctors were obliged to serve one week in camp with the Wehrmacht, and that he was leaving for duty with his unit that day. He had heard of my father and said he was delighted and honoured to meet him. He showed my father over the whole hospital with great pride, commenting that only National Socialismus and the Führer could have made such an achievement possible. My father was deeply impressed by everything: the spacious wards, the modern equipment. He surprised my father by saying that the British Nation must surely be finished, now that their King had abdicated.

Afterwards my father reassured Arthur about the care that Ruth was getting. "I should expect it to be as good as any in the world," he said.

Whether this made Arthur a little less agitated, I don't know. I think his anxiety remained unalleviated.

We saw Aunt Ruth every day of our stay. She never missed an opportunity to sing the praises of the Third Reich. "This is such a wonderful opportunity, Billiam," she said, "for you to see Germany first hand, and I'm sure if you do so with an open mind, you'll agree with me and be thankful that there is one country that will stand up to the Communists. The nuns don't seem to see this at all. They are completely opposed to Hitler. - I tell them, if it weren't for Hitler, the Communists would already be in power and they'd soon shoot the lot of you."

After the visits, there still remained a lot of time to be occupied. We walked all over and round the town, and stood watching soldiers marching. They marched perfectly; they marched as if they were all one body. People stopped on the pavement to see them go by, standing silently, looking through their breath in the cold air. We went in buses up into the hills and through villages, where banners were stretched across the road, with slogans written on them such as 'Dieses Dorf führt nicht nach Jerusalem!' The road to Jerusalem does not lie through this town. 'Wir wollen keine Juden hier.' We want no Jews here.

On many corners people stood collecting for charity. They sold little badges of various sorts. One was a small daisy with a ladybird on it and words saying, 'Help for the poor during the winter months.' The nuns at the hospital, who were anti-Hitler, told us it was no such thing and that all the money went for munitions. Here and there we saw unbelievably poor people, who were blue with cold. They stood in thin clothes begging, in whispered pleas, for money - for it was a punishable offence.

We went up from behind Freiburg in the cable railway, lifted over the pine trees. It was a very tame affair, in spite of the view from the top. We were shown a place half way, where a party of English schoolboys had perished in a blizzard only a short while ago. It seemed unbelievable, rather like dying from exposure in Esher. Suburban houses nestled amongst the trees, with their private drives criss-crossing the hillside. It seems that on their way to the top, the party met a postman coming down, who had warned them of the impending blizzard, but the master in charge took no notice. It is possible that he hadn't quite understood what had been said, and so they died, within a stone's throw of a quaint door knocker, a bird table and a municipal seat erected at the 'Aussichts Punkt'.

We were on our way back from the hospital later than usual. "Hannah," my father said, "you must look and remember!" I did look, and I have always remembered. "Those," he said, "are the Voges Mountains and the frontier of France, and that lighted up cross, is the cross of Lorraine. It is a French War Memorial and a reminder to the Germans when they look up from the Rhine Valley as evening falls. They can hardly help seeing it and remembering the fallen in the war. I hope it never, never happens again." He turned away, and I knew he was sad. I took his hand, and he squeezed mine.

In the war he had been with the Norfolk Regiment, but was

later sent as a pathologist to a huge military hospital near Southampton. The wounded men he had been with were, I believe, an ever present memory, and being in Germany had stirred up the past.

The nuns at the hospital impressed me permanently: their calm devotion, their freedom from wishing to please, their lack of doctor worship. One sister took me to see the children's ward in one of the main blocks. We went there by following the underground network of passages beneath the building. Below ground the atmosphere felt very sinister, and I was afraid. My mother thought so too - it may have been imagination, it may not. Anything could have happened in Germany at that time.

On our last day in Germany, there was a Party Rally. The speeches were relayed on the radio. They blared out from every shop and house - the Führer screamed and raged, thousands stormed enthusiasm - Goebbels and Goering followed. It went on all day. Our hotel reverberated with repetitive 'Sieg Heils'. The porter in the hall shrugged his shoulders in despair. To turn your radio off would have been dangerously obvious, to turn it down, unwise.

My father said, "this thing has permeated the whole place with terror." The Rally was relayed in every part of the hospital - you could hear it everywhere.

We went to say goodbye to Ruth - she was as enthusiastic as ever about the Party. My father found it very tiresome, and dangerous.

Before we left, we sought out the Russian Countess and her son. He was still on crutches. She was very cast down because she had had to get her husband to send some more money from Paris, part of their hard-earned savings. They had stayed longer than their allotted holiday time. The boy hung his head and said in halting English, "We were hoping to buy our mother a coat, but now it is impossible."

We gave them our address in London and the countess wrote down theirs in Paris.

Arthur had found a source of oranges at a little fruiterers on the outskirts of town. He was busy squeezing them, and couldn't spare the time to come to the door and see us off.

We travelled back to Holland in a train that had been named the Rhinegold Express. We were glad to get off it and to sail for home. What a relief it was to get away. What a relief to be back in England and home. How thankful we were.

Bristles was offended that my mother had left him, and his friendship had to be coaxed back. It took a whole meal of raw liver to renew his affection.

CHAPTER 11

My mother had a letter from her sister Evelyn in Shropshire:

'Dear Marion,

I got rather a shock the other day when I realized that Mother is going to be eighty next year.

I really feel that we should give her a slap-up party to mark the occasion. What form it should take, I don't know, but it will have to be at Marchfold. I'm sure you will agree. Whether we should invite people from outside the family, I'm not sure.

Ellen is far too old to manage the cooking or arranging and that's another problem. Perhaps your mad Kitty could be persuaded to go down and do it with the help of someone else; that is, if you don't mind. Or we could get somebody from outside, but that would be so expensive.

When we get together at Christmas we could make all the decisions and draw up plans.

The girls are well, but Sally hurt her knee playing lacrosse a couple of weeks ago - knees are tricky things. Gerald grinds away. He says the only people who seem to be making money these days are butchers. They just rake it in.

If we have a party for Mother, I shall have to have a new evening dress, the two I've got are shamefully tight. I expect you have lots of dresses to choose from - you must need them living in London. (She obviously thought my mother led a gay social life. In fact, she and my father never went anywhere and were always at home.)

Gerald is very worried about Isabella now that civil war proper has broken out in Spain. He says there is no saying where it may lead or what may happen. This is the trouble when relatives marry foreigners - disaster almost always follows.

Evelyn'

There was also a letter from Kate:

'I expect you've had a letter by now from Evelyn. Can you imagine anything more ghastly than a party for Mother? Anyway we're not even supposed to know how old she is. She'll be furious. The whole thing will be so artificial and Ellen and Ivy are far too old themselves to face the appalling shock of such an upheaval. To suddenly make things grand and arranged seems to me totally unnecessary. For one thing, the silver would have to come out of the bank. Anyway who does Evelyn envisage asking? The family and the entire neighbourhood or just the family? We see each other often enough it seems to me, without going to all the trouble of making a special occasion. Of course, we never see Mary, but that goes without saying.

Donald was in London for a meeting with a man and a KC last week - he didn't have time to look in on you.

I heard you went to Germany in the spring. Whatever for?

With love,
Kate'

May wrote:

'What a lovely idea of Evelyn's to celebrate Mother's eightieth birthday. We haven't had any sort of party since our weddings, and it's such fun to dress up and Mother's birthday coming in the spring as it does, makes it even nicer. I had a letter from Kate; she didn't seem too keen, but we must sweep her aside. I hope there won't be any other faint hearts. The expense of course is to be considered, but if we are sensible I'm sure we can keep it down. It depends too on how many people we invite. Booze costs such a lot, that's the trouble.

We've got plenty of time to get it all worked out. After all, it's only October.'

'I'm not against a party for Mother on the whole, but

36

*there do seem to be a lot of almost insurmountable difficulties
to overcome. Like, for instance, where are the big table-cloths
and have we got enough plates? A lot must have got broken
over the years. It's easy to get food together, and easy too, for
it to be disgusting. Do you remember the Wellesley's party with
messed-up salads in bowls that looked just like sick, and the
over-cooked salmon without any sauce to go with it?*

*I must say the more I think of giving this party, the more
daunted I become. Nevertheless, I will back up the enthusiasts.*

*What does Bill think about it? Is it grown-ups only or are
the young to be present?*

Vanessa '

When my father was asked his opinion on the matter he said
he hadn't got one and didn't mean to get drawn into the arguments
anyway.

The autumn came. All our birthdays were in October and
December, except for my mother's. Hers was in April, like Granny
Bell's.

David remembered and sent me a card from Cambridge. I
think it was rather vulgar because my mother put it out of sight.

I became ill and was put to bed. Next day I came out with
the chicken pox, the whole of me was covered with spots, including
under my hair. I asked my mother to bring Bristles up to sit on my
bed and keep me company. He would have none of it and, although
she brought him up three times, he escaped as soon as he could and
ran downstairs.

My bedroom was half of a large, tall Kensington room divided.
It made two passage-like rooms. Ian had one and I had the other. I
had to walk through his to get to mine. My half had the fireplace,
now fitted with a gas fire. There was an elaborate mantelpiece,
where my various treasures were set out: a small pink enamelled
clock that I had had for my birthday, two china cats and a glass
vase that I used when I brought flowers home from the country.

I lay in this room with my chicken pox, looking at the cracks
in the ceiling and the moulded plaster frieze, depressingly cut off by

the cheap division of the room. The walls were painted in a tired yellowing pink and the curtains (which had been bought with the house) were lined, glazed chintz in a grand pattern of plumed birds perched sparsely on decorative, wandering branches. They too showed signs of discoloration.

In my isolation, I sometimes looked out of the window down onto the street. In those days it was almost empty of cars - none were parked. We had a car but it was shut up in a garage on Camden Hill. We never used it in London and only got it out to drive down to the country.

All the big houses were occupied by single families; none of them then were flats.

As I watched, an occasional car drove past, or a taxi bringing somebody home. There was the milkman delivering milk, the coal cart pulled by a horse, a man pushing a barrow and calling out for 'rags and bones'. In the evenings, London characters came along. There was a ragged man who ran down the street writing Bible texts on the pavement with coloured chalks. 'God is Love' was his favourite, only he wrote the 'L' so that it looked like 'God is Cove'. Another man sang strange snatches of a song - always the same song, and a man with a black cape, carrying a guitar, semi-danced his way somewhere. An old man in tattered evening dress with a top hat often walked very, very slowly by at lunchtime. My father once got up from the table and ran after him, gently enquiring if by any chance he was a little hard up. He bowed gallantly and, removing his hat, replied in a cultured voice, "How very kind of you to ask, but, no."

I was very bored, shut up in my room. My father made time to come and read aloud to me. We read The Dancing Floor by John Buchan. It never got finished, because I recovered too quickly.

Ten days later Ian came out in spots. The day he took to his bed, Bristles went up to his room and sat on his feet and stayed all day, every day until he was better.

After our health was restored, we both went back to school, trying to make up for lost time. It was nearing the end of the Christmas term. I rushed home because we were expecting David from Cambridge. Ian had just come in and we were sitting in the schoolroom having tea.

There was a thick fog and David was later than he said he would be. Bristles was sitting by the hissing gas fire, squeezing his eyes together with pleasure.

"How I hate the short days. It's depressing when it gets dark so early," my mother said, "especially when it's foggy, and now the fog is getting into the house. I hope all the windows are shut."

My father remarked that the fog was unusually thick. "But they're not nearly as bad as they used to be when I was young. Then they were real pea-soupers. Every house had a coal fire or fires in those days. Now they mostly have gas."

Ian said, "It's so quiet, I suppose everything's at a standstill. I'm glad I got back before it was quite dark."

My mother, who had become rather fidgety, said, "I expect all the trains will be late. It may be hours before David arrives," and after a pause, turned to my father. "I saw you had a letter from Ruth this morning. What has she got to say?"

"Her walking is not improving as well as they had hoped. Not surprising," my father added, "considering the weight she puts on her leg."

Aunt Ruth and Uncle Arthur had travelled back to England at the end of June, Ruth in a wheelchair. Her leg had taken a long time to mend and she had had to have another operation to remove the wires. My father had arranged a car with a driver to meet them at Harwich and drive them straight to Oxford. Little did they know then that world events and future infirmities would prevent them ever going abroad again.

My father sighed, "I'm afraid Ruth will just have to try and lose a couple of stones."

Suddenly I felt overcome with sadness and fear and my eyes filled with tears while my mouth was full of scone.

My mother asked if anything was the matter.

"No. Why?" I said.

The dreariness of the occasion was at last relieved by the arrival of David. He brought fog in with him and the smell of trains.

We all got up from the tea-table and went to welcome him. He put all his bags and squash racket down in the hall and went straight to the fire to warm his hands and to stroke Bristles, who ignored him completely. Then he sat down and took a scone. My mother poured out tea for him and we shoved the butter and jam in his direction. We were so glad to see him, we were speechless.

"It's taken me ages to get here," he said. "I left Cambridge before lunch. The train was terribly late and the nearer we got to London, the thicker the fog became. It really is a stinker."

We all watched him eat.

"Hannah," he said, "you've grown."

After a while he put his cup down and pushed his plate away and said, "I've something to tell you. Because of what's going on in the world and because of what is likely to happen, I've decided not to go back to Cambridge - I've joined the army."

Then my father said, "Why the army?" and got up and left the room. My father loved David above all others.

It was not until years later that I realized the enormity of the blow and the magnitude of disappointment that David had inflicted on him. Of all emotions, disappointment is probably the most damaging. The very fabric of our family was shaken.

The reason that my father had retired early from the East was so that the boys could be educated at home and not suffer the strain of separation. Our schooling cost all the money that he and my mother had. They hardly ever went anywhere or did anything. Of course, I thought then, that it was because they were old and boring, not because they had no money. Admittedly, we lived in a largish house, but it was in an unfashionable part of London. Both our parents had lived through the First World War and my father had lost his elder brother in the trenches. They had experienced the dread and fear of war. A dread easily revived, as it obviously was, by David's fairly casual announcement.

Next day, David came up to my bedroom.

"I've upset them dreadfully," he groaned.

"Why didn't you talk to them before you did anything, and why didn't you get a degree first and then join the army?" I asked, repeating what I had overheard my father say.

"I knew he'd stop me if I did. You see, I'd made up my mind." His voice became unsteady. "Hannah, I need you to back me up and be on my side. Please. I'm going up to Cambridge on Saturday to collect my things and bring them home. Come with me."

CHAPTER 12

It was Christmas time again. We went down to Marchfold as usual. This time without David. He wasn't going to get leave.

Although we always moaned about the feebleness of the cousins, I really looked forward to seeing them very much. As we got older we had a lot of rowdy fun together. Sylvia was getting to look more like her mother, Aunt Kate. Her angelic blonde nature as giving way to a more robust, ruder and darker presence. I had a secret admiration for Harry, the model boy, whom my brothers found so intolerable.

Granny never had Christmas trees in the house. I once asked her why and she replied that it was a pagan custom introduced into this country by a German. I suppose she meant the Prince Consort. However, we were allowed to decorate the house with holly and ivy. Mistletoe was discouraged because of its vulgar association with kissing.

On Christmas Eve Granny went to the midnight service. A number of us went with her. If the weather was kind, we used to walk across the fields, Granny leading the way with her ever-failing torch. You could see the church lighted up across the river. None of us, of course, knew that it was to be our last Christmas there. The garrulous aunts shattered the quiet night with their endless chattering and laughing as they stumbled along the uneven path in the dark. When returning, they were always less noisy, sometimes silent. I suppose they were tired. Then you could hear the water running under the bridge and the owls hooting in the distance, and enjoy the wonderful smells of mist and frosty air.

The Bells were in a ferment about what they saw as David's disaffection. They talked about it all the time, but not in front of my father. Kate, though, was the exception. Always tactless and rough, she walked into the morning-room, where my father was sitting reading by the fire.

"Will," she said, "you must be in a state of collapse about David. Whatever got into the boy? I am so sorry."

"You needn't be," my father replied, shutting his book impatiently. "I'd much rather that he questioned everything than drifted along on an easy tide."

Kate continued relentlessly, "You're being very philosophical about it. Just as well, because there isn't anything you can do about it. What a waste to throw his education away, not to mention all the money you've put into it. I only hope his life is not going to be weighed down with regrets."

"He may end up a Field Marshall," my father said, opening his book and trying to start reading again.

"Field Marshalls are few and far between," Kate went on. "There are more soldiers than generals, that's the trouble."

After a few moments silence, she got up and left the room rather noisily.

Christmas was not exactly a success that year. To start with Granny said, "I expect it's because I'm getting old, but if you young people (she meant her daughters and their husbands) want to talk about Hitler and the Jews, Mussolini and Italy and Spain and the Communists, could you do it between meals. I don't want to even hear about it. After the sacrifices of the war (she meant the First World War) it's so appalling to think that we're brought to this."

As well, the turkey hadn't been big enough. Some people took more than their fair share of the hot water and didn't take their rightful turn with baths. Others spent too long in the lavatory, keeping people waiting. The husbands were on the whole very non-cooperative and irritable, even refusing to help clear up the wrapping paper from the drawing-room floor after the present opening ritual.

On Boxing Day, Vanessa and Uncle James' Peter developed chicken pox and were banished to bed.

Bessie and Buster went off and didn't come back. Granny was distraught. We all went looking for them, across the fields and along the river, calling all the time. They turned up, muddy and wild, in the early hours of the morning, waking everyone up except Granny, who had not gone to sleep. The day before the family was due to leave, a meeting was called to take place in the morning-room to discuss the arrangements for the approaching 80th birthday party.

44

When everyone was at home, the morning-room was in constant use. It was smaller than other rooms and the peat fire kept it beautifully warm. In the middle was the breakfast table, which was useful to sit round and do things at. Marchfold, just before the war, was a cold place - Granny's dwindling income was beginning to bite and she couldn't afford much heat. That Christmas there had been many murmurings about how icy the house felt. My father pointed out that all the window panes were loose, which made the draughts worse. When my mother asked Granny if she knew about it, she replied, "Of course, the tits have eaten all the putty."

It was late afternoon when the sisters sat round the table to talk. Some of them were chewing pencils. They all had a piece of paper in front of them. I was there sitting by the fire. I was always interested to hear what went on, and took it all in. Because of the shortness of the days, the light had almost gone, partly because the room faced east and missed the last glimmer of daylight.

Over the years, the curtains and upholstery of the room had been slowly destroyed by the rays of the early morning sun. The yellow silk of the curtains hung away from the lining in long shreds. Almost like burnt flesh. The chair covers were faded and balding. Through the french windows you could dimly see the little patch of garden in the twilight outside. It was enclosed by high yew hedges and planted with lavender and various herbs and at this time of year it looked very uninteresting and rather muddy.

Evelyn, who had instigated the whole birthday party idea, was the first to say anything. She had a soft voice and Kate told her sharply to "speak up". "Don't mumble Evelyn," she shouted. After discussing the table-cloths and cutlery, they went on to the food and wine and eventually arrived at the touchy subject of expense. Some felt they were less able to pay than others and, although Mary was almost certainly not going to be there, it was decided that she should be written to and shamed into making a generous contribution.

"After all," Kate said, "she's rolling in money."

"You mean HE is rolling in money, not her, which is a very different thing," Vanessa reminded them.

It became clear to me that Mother hadn't told any of them

about the drama that she had been involved in with Mary. They knew nothing about it at all.

May got up to draw the curtains. Everybody shouted, "What do you think you're doing, they won't stand being pulled!"

At last it came to the delicate subject of who was to be invited and who not.

Granny's sister Pamela must somehow be got from Yorkshire to Marchfold: the answer was a hired car.

"She can easily afford it," Vanessa said, "but why doesn't Kate bring her? After all, she's not far away. The only thing of course is that a larger car would be more comfortable with her leg."

Pamela was now a widow. Great Uncle Donald had been dead three years. I remembered seeing him when I was very little. He took me on his knees and stroked my hair and said what a dear little girl I was. I squirmed with embarrassment and got down as soon as I could get free. He was very old fashioned with a watch chain across his waistcoat and he took snuff, so that the hairs in his nose were orangy-yellow. They had no children, and this had been a perennial grief to both of them. Poor Great Aunt Pamela had bouts of depression and took to her bed several times a year for days on end. Granny Bell was very unsympathetic, having been pregnant for years and years, and referred to her sister's difficulties as 'Pamela's whims'.

The late Great Uncle Donald too came in for a lot of disapproval - for one thing, he was a mill owner. Not only did he have a North Country accent, he owned a satanic mill where people died coughing because of the cotton fluff and back-breaking hours. "Up there," Granny told us often, "the sky is darkened and the sun rarely gets through; the people have pale faces and the white sheep have turned black," adding, "I never can imagine why she married him. Even when he was young, he was ponderous. Anyway he's dead now, poor old blighter. I can't think why Pamela has grieved so desperately over his departure."

No conclusion was reached about transporting Pamela, so the meeting moved on to the neighbours:

"Mr. and Mrs. Jeffries?" - "Of course," they all agreed.
"The Colonel and Diana?" - "Oh, yes."
"Lady Margaret?" - "Certainly."
"The Witherstons?" - "I suppose so."
"Elizabeth and Arthur?" - "Must we?" - "Yes."
"Dr. Black - " "Do we have to?" ... and so it went on.

At last everyone became bored and tired. A few decisions had been taken, but on the whole little progress had been made.

Outside, the night was very black. May got up and turned the light on, which made it blacker.

Kate left the room for a short while and when she came back she announced that she had come upon Granny sitting in the drawing-room window drinking gin and crying. "I said to her, what on earth is wrong with you? Here we all are trying to do things for you and arrange a lovely birthday party, and this is all you do!" "It's very unlike Mother," May observed.

It was New Year's Eve. Seeing the New Year in came into the same category as Christmas Trees with Granny. It was never celebrated or even noticed at Marchfold - such things were only for barbarians north of the border, who drank and whooped and boiled up intestines stuffed with blood and porridge. Therefore, instead of festivities, everyone was drearily packing up ready to leave.

Ellen was being helped to get some supper; then, out of the blue, David arrived. He had walked from Lewis Station. He got a frosty reception from the Aunts, but not from us or Granny. He looked taller and larger. We took him away from the crowd so that we could look at him in private. He hugged us one by one. He had two days leave in which to be with us. The enjoyment was marred somewhat by the knowledge that the two days would soon be gone.

The 1st January 1937 dawned grey and sunless: the exodus began early in the morning. Some travelled by train and had to be taken to the station; others left in their cars. We were staying on for a few days and breathed a sigh of relief with the last goodbye.

That afternoon we had a memorable walk along the river. It had got colder as the day wore on and looked as though it might snow. The boys ragged about, as they always had done, and Ian nearly fell in the river. Granny came with the dogs. When we arrived back at the darkened house, there was only a small glimmer of light from the back kitchen where Ellen and Ivy were sitting in their armchairs in front of the old range, recovering from the shock of having so many visitors.

My mother asked Granny if she could bring Bristles down next time we came - she had become uneasy about leaving him behind in London.

When we left for London a couple of days later, Granny stood beneath the porch on the front steps, Ellen and Ivy behind her, to see us off.

Ian could never bear to say goodbye - he usually hid, or turned the other way.

A week later we heard that Granny was not well. My father travelled down to see her and found that she had shingles. He found her in very low spirits, which was very unlike her.

Meanwhile, arrangements for the birthday party went ahead, in spite of her being so unwell. 'There is plenty of time for her to recover,' Vanessa wrote.

The invitations were sent out, and orders made for this and that. There were more arguments and meetings.

"It's so important to get it all done and set up, to ensure there is no last minute rush," someone remarked.

Our mad Kitty, who had consented to produce the food, was preparing herself for the grand cooking. My mother was anxious and full of misgivings, in spite of Kitty's boastings and descriptions of wonderful, elaborate dishes she created when in service with Lady Balastair. "At Lady Balastair's all the visitors asked where I'd learnt to cook like that. - Not Ireland, surely, they said. No, not Ireland, I said, but from Mr. Wakeford at the Mallet's establishment. He taught me. Great fat man he was, with terrible habits. 'Kitty,' he used to say, 'I show you and you'll never be out of work.' That was before I married. I couldn't have known then that my husband would walk off and leave me with Peggy."

CHAPTER 13

Granny Bell died.

It was such a shock, that I didn't really know what it meant. My mother and father went to the funeral. I don't know what happened, because I wasn't there, and they were too upset to talk about it afterwards.

They came back the same night, bringing Mary and her husband Douglas home to London with them. They had travelled down from Scotland for the funeral.

Seeing my Uncle Douglas sitting by the fire in the schoolroom, reading The Times, it was difficult to imagine him beating his wife and raging mad. He looked so kind and quiet - his complexion was somewhat florid though, I noticed.

At first it was thought that Granny had left no will of any kind, but later on an envelope was discovered in her jewel box. On the envelope was written:

MY WILL

Inside was a sheet of headed writing paper -

'I leave all my possessions to be divided equally between my six daughters, with the exception only of my jewellery. I want Hannah to have my diamond brooch and my pearls, but after that, my other granddaughters may choose what they please.

Two years ago, I bought No. 2 Bank Cottages in the village. I bought it with Ellen and Ivy in mind, in case they wanted to retire. If I die before they do, they should go there to live if it is no longer possible for them to remain at Marchfold.

Victoria Bell

Marchfold, 24th February 1934'

At the bottom was added, 'I want darling David to have the globes.' The writing was obviously of a later date, the ink was a different colour and the pen used was thicker.

"She didn't even bother to have it witnessed," Uncle James criticised. "Fortunately, no one is likely to dispute it, or, I trust no one is going to dispute it. I hope we don't run into trouble with the tax people."

It came to light too that there was hardly any Bell money left. During the slump of the twenties and thirties, all shares had dwindled in value and dividends shrunk, so she had been living mainly on capital. The Widow's Pension that she got from the Foreign Office was so pitifully small that she had really no choice. (I realised that the forgotten grandfather must have been in the Foreign Office.) She had also sold pictures and furniture from the house from time to time to keep afloat, and she had cut down her living expenses to the barest minimum. The only thing she spent a little money on were plants for the garden.

The Aunts' husbands were outraged at the revelation. "Why didn't she ask for advice," they said. "Why didn't she sell up and move to a smaller place more suitable and manageable and within her means?" "How irresponsible she was." "How irresponsible," was the chorus.

My mother interrupted, "All these years we have enjoyed going to Marchfold, I don't think she was irresponsible; in spite of all her difficulties, she gave us wonderful times and kept us all together as a family."

The husbands didn't seem to agree.

"And another thing," my mother went on. "Ellen and Ivy have got to be paid now, just as they were before."

No one said, "of course." Someone asked, anxiously, how much their wages were. Ellen got £1 a week and Ivy 25 shillings.

Kate took Granny's two bewildered dogs home with her to Yorkshire.

After the great upset of death, families usually swoop like vultures to devour the spoils. In the case of Marchfold, there were hardly any spoils, only ominous liabilities.

Mr. Deacon from the local Estate Agents, Crowley and Dullet, had been instructed to have the house surveyed. Granny had known Mr. Deacon for many years, and he had acted for her on many occasions. The most recent being when she sold a small paddock by the road to some people newly arrived in the village. He was a pleasant, countrified, tweedy little man with a red face. Kate said of him, "I can't bear ghastly Mr. Deacon, he's so insultingly cheerful."

That the tits had eaten the putty round most of the windows, everyone knew, and that there were damp patches in the passage and along the outer wall of the drawing-room, but, although the family were apprehensive, they were unprepared for the shock that awaited them in the surveyor's report. No one seemed to have noticed that various lifeforms had moved into the house like shadows, settling and feeding on every feature, and spreading year by year.

Most of the family were in the morning-room, waiting for Mr. Deacon to arrive bringing the report. I was there with my parents. I don't think they thought it mattered if I missed school because I was a girl, and they nearly always gave way when I asked if I could go with them.

It was a sharp April morning. There was no fire in the grate and it was icy cold. The house already felt as though no one lived in it, although Ellen and Ivy were still huddled in the kitchen.

"We should have lighted a fire," May grumbled, "or at least had one of the oil stoves going."

"Rather late to think of that," Kate snapped. "We can't start fiddling about with oil cans and wicks at this stage of the game." She sniffed because her nose was running. Mr. Deacon arrived a little late. He pushed the morning-room door open and apologised. He was not his usual jolly self, but was using his 'recently bereaved' manner.

"Good morning to you," he said soberly, and looking round the grim company, continued, "We are all feeling the loss of Mrs. Bell, I'm sure; I know I am." There was a silence.

He pulled up a chair, sat down and opened his briefcase, took out some papers and put them on the table.

"This is the surveyor's report," he said, holding it up. "I don't suppose its contents will be a surprise to any of you. I'm afraid I have to tell you that the roof is in a very perilous condition indeed - far worse than it appeared at first. I'm sorry to say that to repair it

51

is going to cost a great deal of money." He paused " ... and easily as serious is the drawing-room floor. The beams in the cellar, holding it up, are completely rotten. The whole thing will have to come down. I wouldn't be exaggerating if I told you that it is in a highly dangerous state.

He handed Uncle James, who was sitting beside him, the report. "I suggest," he continued, "that all of you read it through. There is a certain amount of repair needed also to the drains. And now there is the question of No. 2 Bank Cottages; I understand that you didn't know that it belonged to Mrs. Bell until you read her will. Mrs. Bell purchased the cottage a couple of years ago for something like £100. A Mrs. Carter was living there at the time - you may remember her. She died about 8 months ago, so the place has been lying empty since then, and I've no idea what sort of a state it is in. Mrs. Bell's solicitors must have the deeds. They acted for her, I remember, through us. If you wish, I could go and look over the cottage when I'm passing and see what it's like. I think Mrs. Bell must have had the keys."

The gloom was intense.

Mr. Deacon left.

We had brought a thermos of soup and some sandwiches; some of the others had got buns of various sorts and apples and cold sausages. It was a cheerless meal.

Evelyn suggested that we go and have a look at the cottage. Kate was against it. "We shall only be even more depressed. One ruin is quite enough for one day, and, anyway we don't know where the keys are. We'll only be able to look through the windows."

The row of cottages were almost opposite the church, above the road, up a steep grassy bank. Homely smoke was coming from all the chimneys except No. 2, which was at the end of the row. Once they had been thatched, my mother told us, but the thatch had been replaced not long ago by slate tiles. We clambered up the steps and went into the tiny front garden. A small painted gate had fallen off its hinges and lay beside the path. Some daffodils were growing through its bars. We shaded our eyes at the windows trying to see in. Then Kate turned the front door handle. It was unlocked and pushed open rather stiffly, sticking on the stone flagged floor inside. In those days there was little need to bolt and bar places. It was unusual for people to interfere with other peoples' property. We crowded into the small empty front room. There was a blacked grate with two ovens to one side. There was a smell of soot. At the back of the house was a scullery with a large copper for boiling washing, and there was a sink and a single cold tap. An enclosed staircase with a door at the bottom led up to the bedrooms. The larger of the two faced south and looked across to the church and the churchyard. You could see where the river went, and beyond the fields, to where Marchfold stood squarely amongst its trees and gardens.

The back door was locked, so we went round the side of the cottage to get into the garden. It was very overgrown by brambles and nettles that were just beginning to sprout. At the bottom of the plot was the lavatory in its decrepit wooden shack, covered by ivy and overgrown with privet bushes. A strong row of rhubarb was just beginning to show.

May said, "It would be impossible for Ellen and Ivy to live here at their age. They'd never be able to manage."

"I don't see why not," Kate observed. "I think it could be very cosy and it's got such a jolly view. Anyway, if they don't come here, where are they to go when Marchfold is sold?"

All Granny's personal possessions had to be valued for death duties. I remember seeing her clothes laid out in her bedroom, like faded thrown-away flowers. There were rows of satin shoes with silver and gold buckles and little waisted heels. The sad progress of the female body was there to be seen - the early dresses had 18" waists, but as time went by the inches increased and increased.

After the valuation was completed my mother was determined to make a funeral pyre next to the compost heap and burn all the clothes, together with other intimate things that had belonged to Granny. This she did without asking or telling her sisters.

Kate was furious when she found out. "I heard of a woman the other day in Brighton who hires out fancy dress and I'm told she gives very good prices for things of quality and in good condition."

"Not all of them were in good condition," my mother said feebly.

"And what have you done with the thirty pairs of gloves? Those beautiful French gloves!"

"I'm afraid they've gone too," my mother admitted. "I didn't like to think of her things wandering around the world without her."

There had always been gentle squabbling amongst the sisters, but now for a while began the onslaught of the most terrible and serious quarrelling.

We went to Marchfold every weekend after this to try and put things into some sort of order and to see how Ellen and Ivy were getting on.

My father and mother went through Granny's desk and all her papers. There were hardly any outstanding bills, all the ones needing to be paid were recent. She had kept all the letters that I had ever written to her, and Ian's and David's as well. Not that there were many of them, I have to admit, but in the bottom drawer at the back were a whole bundle of letters tied together with tape. They began 'Darling Vicky' and were signed 'Fawn'. Whether that was my grandfather's nickname or someone else's no one seemed to know. My father didn't read them or let anyone else even look at them. In retrospect, I think it was a terrible mistake not to keep them and read them. What insight we might have gleaned about Granny and her life. What colour might have been induced into our ideas about her. But they were thrown onto the bonfire; the fire devoured them and the flames carried the ash upwards for the wind to blow away.

Efforts were made to get in touch with the relatives of Ellen and Ivy, without much success. A nephew was found in Battle and he was willing to have his aunt, but wouldn't take on Ivy as well. Mr. Norton, the dreadful Norton, had been instructed to keep an eye on the old ladies. He stoked the range and brought in the coal, but the day came when he announced that he had got himself another job and would be moving at the end of the month.

So it was decided to move the old ladies into the cottage that Granny had intended for them come what may. They had been completely unnerved and lost by her death and cowered in the kitchen to see that all the doors and windows were secured. The repairing and redecorating of the cottage was put in hand urgently. The chimney had to be swept because of the starlings, the outdoor lavatory cleared of nettles and the door rehung. Curtains had to be adapted, the front gate replaced and furniture brought from the house; iron bedsteads and chests of drawers from their bedrooms and tables and chairs from what had once been called the servants' hall. It was a terrible day when they eventually moved out of Marchfold; their old-fashioned domed trunks with their names painted on were brought downstairs and loaded on Mr. Taylor's cart. Both of them were crying.

It was expected that they would die of shock within a week, but to everyone's amazement they settled in quickly, seemed to become younger, and took on a new lease of life. They were very proud of their new home. Their neighbours were kind to them and helped them in every way possible, while declaring with righteous indignation how shameful it was to turn two old ladies into the countryside after a lifetime of service.

I suppose they were not nearly as old as I thought they were. When you're fourteen, anyone over 25 is ancient.

After Ellen and Ivy had gone we moved into the kitchen for warmth and convenience. We cooked and ate our meals there and sat round the range in the evenings.

As the year progressed, spring moved in, flooding the rooms with sunlight. Those short times at Marchfold were very happy in spite of Granny's death. I had accepted the fact that she had died and, strangely, didn't miss her at all, but I did miss the dogs - especially Bessie, because I knew they were alive somewhere else with Aunt Kate and I longed to run about with them and play as I always had done.

Almost imperceptibly disorder had crept into the garden. You could see that Granny had gone, but it didn't seem to matter. By then Norton did nothing to speak of. He sat in the potting shed smoking or did a bit of clipping here and there to appear busy when we were about. We avoided him as best we could because he was such a terrible talker and once he got you, it was almost impossible to get away.

It was settled that when the house was sold Ellen and Ivy should be bought a small annuity. In the end, I think they were persuaded by their immediate neighbours that they really had been hard-done-by and they became less pleased to see us and our visits became less frequent.

A sort of hysteria grasped the family. At one of the endless meetings, Kate brought up the subject of the globes.

"They are one of the few really desirable things in the house," she said. "I know Mother wanted David to have them, but I hope, for the sake of family unity, he will decide of his own accord to waive his right to them."

There were other objections to me having the diamond brooch and pearl necklace. My mother refused to give way entirely and insisted that I have the brooch, but suggested that Sally should have the pearls. This brought Vanessa into the fray.

"What about Susan?" she shouted, her voice rising in a crescendo of protest.

When it came to the sale, the globes in fact made hardly anything, and neither did anything else. Where the family got the idea that they would fetch a lot of money I don't know, but nothing made money at that time. If the same things were sold now, I expect the contents of the house would easily have topped a million pounds.

The date for the sale and the contents of the house was fixed. There was a viewing day beforehand. I wasn't present, but was told afterwards how dreadful it was to see the neighbourhood picking over Granny's belongings. A lot of people had come purely out of curiosity to poke about and see for themselves what the house was like inside.

Two women were overheard talking in Granny's bedroom. "It was said that it was in a bad state of repair," one remarked, "but I had no idea how dilapidated it really was."

"I've heard that she was a weird sort of woman," the other said. "She was pointed out to me once at a flower show in the village hall. She had egg on the front of her blouse!"

It was very upsetting to hear Granny talked about so disrespectfully, and my mother returned to London very subdued and sad. She said she was sure that the ladies talking must have come from sea-front flats somewhere - possibly Hove. She further described them to me as having gruesome faces, deeply engrained with make-up, and being manacled and shackled by masses of appalling glass and brass jewellery and as having huge earrings like microphones, and as well as that, they flourished long red threatening talons.

"Why do you think people like that bother to go to Granny's house, or the village flower show, for that matter?" I asked, and my mother replied firmly, "Because people like that don't know how to keep their proper place."

When the sale was over, the house lay entirely empty and was then put on the market. For the first time in our lives, we had nowhere to go to in the country and were entirely London-bound. We went down one Sunday afternoon and wandered through the echoing rooms. I felt it very sadly belonged to the past, which of course it did.

After all this had happened, a great change came about in our lives. A sort of domestic revolution.

CHAPTER 14

The servants in London continued to be endlessly quarrelsome. Mad Kitty seemed to be getting worse, if that were possible. A new recruit to the household, a Czechoslovakian Communist, stormed out in the middle of the night. It was this, I think, that made my father decide to send them all away, with the exception of Mrs. Norton, who was to stay and count the laundry, open the front door and oversee daily cleaners at their work.

From then on we moved down into the basement to do our own cooking and to eat.

"We were very happy when we moved into the kitchen at Marchfold when Ellen and Ivy left, so why not here in London?" my father said.

The situation was not really in any way similar. At Marchfold the kitchen looked across the sunny stable yard. In London it was well below the street, but my father was not in any way daunted and set about making it as pleasant as possible.

First, the old cooking range was taken out, revealing shovelsfull of black beetles. The coke boiler was removed and replaced by a huge thermostatically-controlled gas water heater. It was the latest and most modern thing at that time - it roared intermittently, the blue jets exploding into life.

A long refectory table was bought and a Welsh dresser and my father commissioned an artist who worked in stainless steel to make plates and dishes; each piece was hand-beaten and had an incised line round the rim. They looked splendid on the dresser, but proved to be a social catalyst and a constant cause of criticism and complaint. My father pointed out their wonderful qualities to visitors when they sat down at the table.

"Not only do they look beautiful," he explained, "but they are indestructible and will last forever."

He didn't go on to say that when heated they got red hot and then cooled so quickly that, before you could finish your food, any gravy or sauce solidified into little patterns in front of you.

The first casualty of the stainless steel plates was Mrs. Norton.

"I cannot see myself eating off of common tin plates, like what they have in the army," she said, and gave in her notice.

Ruth and Arthur came on a short visit to see a doctor. They also were offended by the plates. Since coming home from Germany, Arthur had retired into his former habit of silence, and he startled us by suddenly saying, "Eating off those plates makes me feel like a mediaeval villain."

Ruth sniffed - she had become quite irritable since her accident - "I hardly think they would have had stainless steel, dear," she retorted, "but I do have to agree with you up to a point. For one thing, apart from being so basic, they are so painfully noisy. Scraping away after one's food sounds almost like a railway goods yard."

Ruth also thought eating in the basement very unacceptable. She didn't like seeing my father doing the cooking either, and told my mother so, in no uncertain terms.

"Not only is it unsuitable," she said, "it is so inexplicably eccentric. I don't like to see a distinguished man like Billiam wasting his time on domestic chores. The whole set-up is so peculiar: all below ground in this depressing twilight and seeing the legs walking past through the railings above where the sky ought to be."

When Vanessa saw the plates she was enchanted and ordered some for herself straight away.

"I saw them in Sweden when we were there two years ago, and I've always wanted them since then," she said. Kate was enthusiastic too.

Bristles was hopelessly confused by our move below stairs. He sat in his favourite chair in the dining-room underneath the portrait of great, great, great aunt Sophie, waiting for meals to be brought. After some days, when none came he followed us down into the basement. There he found himself a new position on the shelf at the end of the dresser.

After Mrs. Norton's departure, a lady was sent to us from one of the agencies. She was half-German and half-French. She had married an Englishman during the 1914 war. She had met him while he was shut up in an internment camp in Germany. When the

60

war ended she came to England with him. His health had been badly undermined by his imprisonment and his family refused to even acknowledge the existence of his German bride. They too were of German origin and had changed their name from Kapp to Capp, in an effort to hide the act and keep themselves from being penalised and abused. Within a year the young husband was diagnosed as having TB. He was packed off to a sanatorium in Switzerland, where he lingered for about five years. His widow found herself alone and adrift amongst the other thousands of unattached women left by the recent slaughter. The most unhappy part of her story was that she couldn't go back to Germany, involved as she had been with British internees and prisoners of war. She had risked her life time and again to help them escape, and therefore felt that, as a traitor, she might easily be subjected to a firing squad. In spite of all this, she retained her Germanness and could never conceal her pride at the resurgence of her country under Hitler.

She arrived with very few possessions, just two suitcases and a hat. She was short and rather stocky with dark curled hair and very blue eyes. I realise now that she must have only been in her middle thirties. Then I accepted the idea that her life was all in the past (I'm afraid I was right, as it turned out). She came to us as Mrs. Capp, but it wasn't long before we started calling her Fritzie. How that nickname came about, I don't know.

She told us that her father had been a successful opera singer, but tragedy had struck. He lost his voice at the height of his career and their fortunes changed sadly from opulence and social prominence to depletion and oblivion.

While Fritzie was with us, her niece - a famous soprano - came to England to sing at Glyndbourne. Transformed in floating finery, she trundled down to Sussex to hear her. She related later how she had been carried away by the music and the beauty of the garden into the realms of all the things that might have been.

When Ruth heard this, she was incredulous, but after talking to Fritzie, was persuaded that it was true. Fritzie, though, sensed that her word was being doubted and didn't reply to her in German, but in her peculiar English. She didn't exactly speak with a foreign accent, rather her words fitted badly into the sentences. Anyway she never forgave Aunt Ruth, and always spoke of her to me as 'that dashing Ruth woman'.

It is sad for me to think of Fritzie now. Her constant ailments and 'rheumatisms', her constant fear of developing TB, which I dismissed cruelly as 'foreign fussing'. Her days off were spent on visits to the German Hospital. She was never satisfied with my father's diagnosis of her ailments, and only had confidence in what the doctors at the German Hospital had to tell her.

Fritzie was always endless fun and there was never a dull moment. I learnt German from her and was able to talk to her brother when he came on a visit to London from Hamburg, where he had a shop that sold oriental rugs. He was a big man with a beard whose main interest in life was in music.

David came home on leave. He had been made a lance-corporal. He was very upright and strong-looking and my father was obviously immensely proud of him.

Shortly afterwards he was plucked out of the ranks of the East Surrey's and went to Sandhurst. I don't know how this came about - whether it was to do with my father or Cambridge, or something else, I have no idea.

Ian did very well in his school certificate, passed his 'little go' satisfactorily and had gone up to Cambridge. We went and spent the day with him and saw his rooms which were in an old timbered house in the middle of town. His landlady, Mrs. Warminger, was hugely fat with a passion for green. Not only did she dress in pond green, but Ian's rooms were all decked out in it as well. Far from being pleasant, it had a sickly, stagnant feel about it. He didn't seem to have made the rooms his own at all, but then he hadn't been there long.

We went down to the Backs. My father wanted to hire a boat, so that we could row down the river, but it was October and the boats had been put away for the winter. We sat on the grass and watched the water flow past. It was a warm and sunny day, but it was truly autumn.

As we were leaving, my father said, "I don't want to come

here again, there are too many ghosts."

I remember we sat in silence going back to London on the train. I was the only one left at home now. I wondered why my father had said that about the ghosts, particularly as he had always told me how much he had enjoyed his Cambridge days. I thought Ian seemed rather lonely. I looked at my mother sitting opposite me in the train. Her hair was going very grey, almost white in the front, and I was suddenly in agony at the thought of her being very old and possibly dying.

CHAPTER 15

When we arrived home, we found that Fritzie had made a goulash, ready and waiting for our return. It was a nice surprise - she was new to us and we were new to her, but during the meal she suddenly became very sullen and moody. Afterwards, we whispered amongst ourselves, behind closed doors (just like the aunts at Marchfold) and racked our brains to think what could have been the cause. Whatever faults our family had, they were never moody. We weren't used to moods. Later, I found out that it was because we weren't appreciative enough of the stew - we learnt then always to say how marvellous it was of her to do anything.

We missed not being able to get out of London more and more. Eventually, my father wrote to several estate agents asking for details of cottages to let in Sussex.

Envelopes came full of dreary photographs and descriptions of various properties, many of which had no plumbing of any sort, and only a few had baths.

It was almost winter by then, but we drove down Saturday after Saturday to look at the most promising ones. The extraordinary thing was that nearly all the roads seemed to lead to Marchfold.

There was one lovely cottage deep in the fields, that could only be reached by going through a farmyard and then a rick yard. It was owned by a small thin woman with very artistically done hair. She explained it at once by telling us she was an artist. We would have known anyway because her unpromising canvases were all over the walls and propped up against everything. She showed us over the place, and, opening an upstairs window, pointed to the trees in the distance. "Over there is a house called Marchfold," she said, "it belongs to a family called Bell. The old lady who lived there has just died and it's up for sale. They say it's in a very bad state. Evidently the family lived very much above their means and couldn't afford to do the simplest repairs. They used to give lavish parties for the county and could hardly afford a car."

Poor Granny never had parties and hardly ever had anyone

even to lunch. She had lived in almost semi-isolation when the family weren't there.

The idea of taking somewhere in sight of Marchfold was intolerable.

Our search stopped being a pleasure and became increasingly tedious. The weather had got bad and many of the little houses that we looked over were empty and damp, and we arrived home several times dispirited and very cold, so we decided to wait until the spring before resuming our hunt.

A letter came from Ruth:

> 'Dear Billiam,
>
> You told me you had started to look for a place in the country to rent. I know you would prefer to be in Sussex, possibly just because you know it, but a great friend of mine (Pamela Moreton) has died and her daughter, who is in India with her husband, has entrusted me to find a suitable tenant for her mother's house. She would like to let it on a five year lease and might consider selling it later on.
>
> The cottage is in a village called Stunford Bowton in north Oxfordshire, on the Warwickshire border. It is on the edge of the Cotswolds and only eight miles from Banbury; there is an excellent train service to Paddington from there, which would relieve you of the strain of driving down every time.
>
> The little house, called Chapel House, is on a sharp hill and has a delightful cottage garden that slopes to a field which falls again steeply to a stream and oak trees. A ha-ha separates the garden from the field, where farm animals picturesquely graze from time to time. Pamela was an enthusiastic and knowledgeable gardener, and it is planted with a great variety of interesting plants.
>
> I expect you would have liked it to be furnished, but I'm afraid everything was sold by auction not long since, so it is empty. I think it was a pity, but that is what Pamela's daughter wanted done.
>
> Let me know if you're interested and I'll make

arrangements for you to see over it. I might even meet you there myself; after all, it's not that far from Oxford.

Arthur has been troubled by boils again - it is very worrying. There is talk of having a vaccine made, but it sounds very dangerous to me. We might like to seek your opinion if they don't clear up soon.

> *Yours affectionately,*
> *Ruth'*

After reading the letter, my father remarked that he didn't like the bit about 'after all it's not that far from Oxford'. But he wrote back thanking her for her letter and 'for letting us know about the cottage. It was very kind of you to think of us.'

We gave it no more thought. The weather had got bad and we had given up house-hunting, anyway for the time being.

CHAPTER 16

That year we had our first Christmas on our own in London. Our first Christmas free of family tensions and chilblains. But, however hard we tried to persuade ourselves, these pluses didn't take away my longing to be with Granny in Sussex, and I'm sure my mother felt the same. We even had a Christmas tree, which we had never had at Marchfold because of Granny's disapproval.

Fritzie spent Christmas Day with a revered elderly German friend who lived in Surbiton.

Bristles never celebrated religious festivals, and always made himself scarce.

It was 1938 - all through '37 fear was mounting. Children in schools were photographed by the press doing gas-mask drill - Hitler and Mussolini were talking of expanding their empires. I read how on 1st August that year Heinrich Himmler opened a concentration camp called Buckenwald to achieve 'unity and capacity', whatever that might mean. Non-Nazi parents risked having their children taken from them. The Chancellor, Herr Hitler, declared 'children belong to the nation'. On 29th August Japanese bombers relentlessly bombed Shanghai. This was to clear the way for their advancing forces. But Shanghai was a long way away - the other side of the world. What the Japanese did didn't affect us directly and, anyway, being in the Far East, what did it matter to us?

The House of Commons got the go-ahead to build air-raid shelters. In Spain Franco was beginning to win the Civil War.

Of course, I only heard adults talking, and still thought secretly that it was all very exciting.

One day, towards the end of winter, my mother suddenly suggested that we drive to Banbury and on to see the cottage at Stunford Bowton. "We won't tell Ruth, we'll just go and have a look at it, even if we can't get in." My father got the map of Oxfordshire out and found the village.

It took us three and a half hours to get to Banbury Cross, there we turned up a hill, past the huge, menacing red-brick workhouse, then out into the beautiful, bleak rolling countryside.

After passing through the villages of Kerston, Lowberry and Sulster, we turned off the Shipston Road, and down a dreary narrow lane. On the right was rising ground covered with scrub, and on the left were derelict fields. Later we learnt that it was called 'Corpse Lane'. Stunford had no church or burial ground of its own. The dead had been carried that way to Sulster since early times. Only recently had a church been built in the village.

After driving about three-quarters of a mile, we climbed a sudden small hill with cottages huddled at the top. We found Chapel House easily enough. An old man came out of the cottage next door - "Mrs. Attwood's over there. She's got the key," he said.

We found Mrs. Attwood. She looked at us with a 'cold, unnerving stare'. "I haven't heard from Mrs. Colville about giving anyone the key," she said haughtily. "But I suppose it's alright. I'll put my coat on and come round."

It is extraordinary to think that as late as 1938 there could have been anyone left, dressed as she was. She could not have been more than sixty-one or two. She was handsome and upstanding, her thick greyish hair twisted up on her head in a very stylish way. She had wonderfully fine features and a really beautiful face - strangely, it never showed that she had no teeth and didn't wear false ones. She wore a white blouse with a high collar edged with lace, a long skirt protected by an enveloping apron, and black lace-up boots.

My father was always so good at putting people at their ease, and as he started to walk back towards the house, she began to thaw a little. By the time she had fitted the key into the front door lock, she had grown almost friendly.

Inside it was very dark and smelt, as empty houses do, of damp and of the past. In the old part of the house, all the floors were flagged stone. There were steps down into a light oakbeamed kitchen; an enclosed staircase (like Ellen and Ivy's) branched from a little landing in two directions to four bedrooms.

Mrs. Attwood explained, "She got so as she couldn't go upstairs the last five years, so she had this built. There's a bedroom and a bathroom and what 'er called the sunroom, looking down the garden. 'Er daughter made 'er do it. There was no bathroom afore that."

We went into the sitting-room (the sunroom) and glanced over the garden. It looked nothing but an earthy, muddy flowerbed. The unusual plants were wisely still underground, a few rose bushes straggled, and an old apple tree, with propped branches, grew to one side. The ha-ha was as Aunt Ruth described it in her letter. Across the tops of the leafless trees in the valley you could see the rest of the village on the opposite hill - little wisps of smoke rising from the chimneys, amongst the winter orchards and gardens.

Mrs. Attwood locked the front door as we left.

"One thing is certain," my mother said, as we drove away, "absolutely certain - we could never go there."

* * * * *

The first warm day brought the crocuses out in London.

As I was getting ready to go to school, my mother said, "your father and I have decided to go and have another look at Ruth's cottage. We won't be back by the time you get home from school, but we expect to be back shortly after."

They were very late getting home. Fritzie and I had our meal together. Bristles sat on the area steps and refused to come in. I was glad when I heard them arrive. We had kept their supper hot for them, and after they had sat down to eat, they told us all that had happened.

It had been altogether a beautiful day - Mrs. Attwood had given them the key and they went alone to the house, where they wandered over it, dreaming. The garden was coming to life, and great clumps of distinguished plants were beginning to come up. Under the yew tree, by the kitchen window, there was a patch of winter aconites, nearly over. Growing out of the stones that bordered the central brick path were some sweet scented irises. A spring haze hung over the countryside, cows were grazing in the field below the ha-ha and, after being in London all winter, the whole experience breathed release and romance.

The next day my father posted a letter to Ruth.

'We have been twice to see Chapel House,' he wrote. *'If it hasn't already been taken by someone else during our indecision and delay, we would be grateful if you could make arrangements for us to sign the lease.'*

His letter was dated 13th March. On 14th, Hitler marched into Austria.

The lease was duly sent to us and signed by my father.

Ruth wrote:

'I am delighted to be able to think of you now as almost neighbours. When you have made all your arrangements for moving into Chapel House, do let me know and, if it is at all possible, I will drive over.

I will also write to some of Pamela's friends in the village and ask them to call on you. The parson, Mr. Havers, is a classical scholar of some merit and very well worth knowing. At the far end of the village towards Lipston, there are three maiden ladies. They live at Border House. Pamela described them to me as being of gentle birth and very well read.

When last in London I was rather distressed to see that Hannah presented rather a slovenly appearance. I noticed that she had a hole in her skirt. First impressions are of great importance in a new place I feel.

Arthur has not had a recurrence of boils now for over two months. My knee is still very stiff. I suppose it is because of having to have it in plaster for so long.'

Pleasantries were exchanged, but beneath everyday arrangements and living, fear was increasing day by day. Immediately after the Anschluss, the Jewish people of Austria were subjected to a vicious onslaught of brutality. A programme called 'The Great Spring Cleaning' by the Nazi newspapers was carried out against the Jewish population.

My parents travelled round the countryside attending various sales and bought furniture, crockery and the things needed for Chapel House, all the time bemoaning the fact that the same objects they were buying had recently been almost given away at Marchfold.

On 10th April Hitler held a plebiscite in Germany and Austria. It was officially announced later that 99% of the people voted in favour of the Anschluss - the unification of Austria with Germany. All the voters came out of the voting stations wearing a badge, each with 'One Führer' displayed on it.

On 2nd May the Prime Minister, Mr. Chamberlain, signed a pact with Italy. He spoke enthusiastically about the new Italy under the vigour of Signor Mussolini. The deal included the recognition of Italy's annexation of Abyssinia and the Italian promise to withdraw troops from Spain.

We moved into Chapel House, one weekend towards the end of May. We got there at about midday, but the removal van didn't arrive until 6 o'clock in the evening. When night came, we were still surrounded by packing cases and newspaper and unmade beds. It was a chaotic mess. I thought it was great fun, but I expect my parents thought otherwise.

We found some coal in an outhouse and lit a fire in the kitchen grate.

We had unpacked our new cooking stove which was a paraffin 'Valour Perfection' - dreadful in its brilliant bright blue enamel. I was not then initiated into the art of trimming wicks, or into the secrets of yellow ragged flames that plopped. The beauties of blue and even flames were unknown to me, as were the horrors of rogue spikes that smoked and blacked the rooms and choked the air.

My mother and father had chosen to use the downstairs bedroom. I was upstairs in the smallest of the four rooms. Its window opened onto the large flat leaded roof of the new sitting-room. When I went to bed that night, I climbed out for the first time and gazed down on the garden and beyond, over the fields and into the distance. Misty and vague in the moonlight, the great old apple tree below was in flower, covered with blossom. It looked white, almost as if snow were on the branches. I sat, remembering Marchfold and the sounds that I had listened to there when I was lying in bed. Here, it was deeply quiet. I could just hear the stream at the bottom of the little valley and a horse pulling grass beyond the garden. I sat and sat, looking and breathing, until the cold drove me in.

The next day was a Saturday, and we drove into Banbury to buy a few things that we needed. Wherever we went my father would talk to people. I was very embarrassed by him, and wished with all my heart that he wouldn't make himself so conspicuous.

During the afternoon, we explored the village as far as the Post Office, which we found shut. On the way we only met one sullen man, and he turned away and wouldn't speak. I found out afterwards that our progress had been watched intently, and had been discussed in minute detail.

"They've taken over Mrs. Moreton's house as a weekend cottage. Fancy people they are, from London. They say he's a doctor from abroad."

On Sunday Mrs. Attwood came. She and her husband had killed a pig two days earlier. She produced an old discoloured plate upon which was some brawn she had made. It was a gesture of friendship.

"I could come and work for you in the mornings if you like, and look after the house when you're not here. Our Dad could do the digging for you now and again, if it suits." That was how Mrs. Attwood came into our lives.

Before we left Stunford, the house was more or less in order, though some of the windows lacked curtains and we needed some matting for the kitchen floor.

A letter came from Ruth:

'Dear Billiam,

I was very sorry not to be able to come over to Stunford last weekend and see you move in, but I had to give lunch to some distinguished visitors from America.

I hope the move went well. The weather was kind anyway.

I wrote to the Havers and told them that you had rented

Pamela's house. I wrote as well to the Misses Bates.

You must have made the acquaintance by now of the stalwart Mrs. Attwood. I think she may prove very useful to Marion in the future.

I trust Hannah has taken heed of the remarks I made in my last letter.

I feel I really must do something about my knee. Is it alright if we come to London the week after next? If this is convenient, I will make an appointment with Mr. Graves.'

It was two months before Ruth could get an appointment with her leg man. He was away in America, so it was already summer by the time they came to London. I noticed that she no longer glided as of old, but almost lurched in a painful and ungainly way. My father was not very sympathetic to her and said sharply, "You know Ruth, you really must get back to walking normally. It is no wonder that your knee hurts. It wouldn't do any harm to lose a bit of weight as well."

After the consultation, Ruth was very cast down and would say nothing. Arthur said to my father that they had been told that the possibility of any great improvement in her leg was unlikely, and that she had probably got to live with the inconvenience and discomfort for the rest of her life, adding that Mr. Graves had nothing but praise and admiration for the skill and success of the German surgery which enabled her to walk as well as she could.

"The arteries are the complication," Arthur said gloomily.

During this visit, all meals had to be carried up to the playroom because Ruth couldn't manage the basement stairs. I suspect that she found eating in the kitchen incompatible and made the most of her disability to her own advantage.

Fritzie became more and more moody by the hour, in spite of the fact that we all helped her bring the food up. Bristles too sat hopefully in the kitchen, waiting for mealtimes as he had before in the dining-room. He became restless and offended. My mother was sure he had a hair ball.

Ruth complained again about the noise that the knives made

75

on the stainless steel plates - "It goes right through me," she said, "I can even feel it in my knee!"

We were having breakfast in the schoolroom. It was a lovely morning and the French windows were open. I remember looking at the hops that grew rampantly over the area railings and along down the basement wall. The roses that my father had recently planted in the side beds were beginning to flower.

"You roses are going to be a great success, Will," my mother remarked.

I was eating fast because I was going to be late for school again.

The telephone rang. My father got up and left the room to answer it.

It was then that Ruth turned to my mother and said, "Marion, I don't like the look of Billiam. He doesn't look well." I could see that my mother was suddenly shocked and afraid.

I left for school. All day I worried about what Ruth had said. It absorbed me entirely, like a raw place on my hand or a knife in my gut. To love is to be sad, but I knew that already.

Ian was back from a cycling tour in France. After supper, everybody was sitting in the garden enjoying the summer evening and talking, except for my father, who was indoors at the top of the house, working in his study. He was preparing to go to a conference in Geneva on malaria being held by what was then the League of Nations. He had been asked to represent Britain. The purpose of the gathering was to examine a claim made by the Germans for an entirely new form of treatment.

"When does Billiam leave for Switzerland?" Ruth asked.

"A week today," my mother answered.

I slipped away and ran upstairs to my father's study. I opened the door and went in. I was out of breath. He was writing at his desk. He raised his head and looked at me over this glasses.

"Hannah," he said, "what do you want?"

"I thought I'd pay you a visit," I said. "You seemed so far away up here, at the top of the house."

Looking at him, I saw at once what Aunt Ruth had seen.

CHAPTER 17

My father died.

David came home immediately.

After the worst was over, we fled from the house and took a train to Ely. Why Ely, I can't think. Perhaps my mother had some secret connection with my father there - I don't know. There we found what was called The Commercial Hotel to stay in. The whole place smelt heavily of beer, pee and tobacco. In the dining-room was a long table covered by a white cloth. Down the middle marched an army of sauce bottles and elaborate silver-plated cruets.

We were the only guests who were not commercial travellers. They were a black-coated, grimy, Dickensian crowd, now of course extinct. I had never seen anyone like them before. They seemed to know each other, but they were not altogether unfriendly to us (if a little awkward), and sometimes offered us different sauce bottles with trickles of sauces round the tops.

I don't think we noticed what we ate.

We sat in the Cathedral to pass the time. The beauty of it was no comfort, although I remember thinking it was like being under beech trees.

We walked along dykes in the rain, treading down the dried grass and the last of the scabious heads. The boys mooned along in apathetic boredom, longing to start living again, but prevented from doing so by my mother's shock and grief, and my querulous dismay and distress.

At the end of the week, David had to go.

My mother said she couldn't face going back to London yet, so the rest of us took a train up to Yorkshire to stay with Aunt Kate. It was a long meandering journey. We had to change several times. It was a stressful day for me because we were mostly travelling in single compartments without lavatories. Ian was very impatient with my agitation.

I had never stayed with Aunt Kate before. It turned out on

the whole to be a therapeutic experience, in spite of her tactlessness and rough manner and the presence of Uncle Walter. Their stodgy ways were very regular and the household went like clockwork. Very different from our way of living.

Bessie and Buster were overjoyed to see me, as I was to see them, but they were sadly changed. They were only allowed out alone in the small garden, otherwise they were taken for walks on leads at regular times. When I asked why, Uncle Walter replied, "Because of the sheep."

There were two lovely country maids in the house; a cook and a red-faced girl called Amy, whose father was a shepherd on a neighbouring estate. Her family lived far from anywhere, and on her afternoon off I accompanied her home. I borrowed a bicycle and we rode together along narrow pot-holed lanes until we reached their cottage. As we arrived, small brothers and sisters rushed out to meet her. Inside, it was steamy with ironing and cooking. Children and animals fell over each other through the open door.

I understood that Amy gave all her wages to her mother week by week. After our arrival, she invariably took the ironing from her mother, heating the flat irons on the fire and spitting on them to test the heat.

'Tea' didn't start until her father came in from work. He shook my hand so hard that it hurt, and made a joke that I didn't understand - I felt my face going red. They all laughed, and I imagined that they looked at me as though I was a pampered curiosity.

We had stew, and afterwards, bread and jam. I felt life coming back into me, but it was soon time to leave. Amy had to be in by 9.30 and wouldn't dare be late.

It was while we were in Yorkshire that Mr. Chamberlain flew to Germany to see Hitler, who had declared his intention of entering German-speaking Sudetenland in Czechoslovakia. He built up war tension by revealing that 462,000 men were working on fortifications in the Rhineland, adding that "the great new fortresses will be ready by winter."

Panic-stricken, our depleted fleet was mobilised. The French called up reservists and rushed to man their new Maginot Line.

Europe held its breath. Poor Mr. Chamberlain said, "I am a man of peace to the depths of my soul. Armed conflict between Nations is a nightmare to me, but if I am convinced that any Nation had made up its mind to dominate the world by fear of its force, I would feel it should be resisted. Under such domination, the life of people who believe in liberty would not be worth living."

When he flew home from Munich after signing an agreement with Hitler, his welcome in London was tumultuous.

"I believe," he declared, "it is peace in our time."

Everyone wanted to believe it of course - who wouldn't - and after all Hitler was only invading a part of Czechoslovakia that was German-speaking. If you didn't think about it too much, it didn't really seem unreasonable. Anyway, war was unthinkable by those who had experienced it before, and impossible by those who hadn't. A new generation of sons had just had time to grow up since the last armistice.

Fritzie rang up and said she was nervous by herself, so Ian was sent back to London to join her. My mother felt it was time for us to go too. Kate had become irritable, probably because of the Munich crisis, and we felt we had outstayed our welcome.

Now, added to my mother's grief was the gripping fear of almost certain war and the dread of losing the boys. She seemed to have forgotten that David was already in the army, until he rang up one evening while we were at Kate's and said, "I hope you realise that war is only postponed. It'll be a relief when it comes, we're all raring to go."

CHAPTER 18

When we got home to London, I went back to school. The other girls looked at me as though I had got a disease. My friend Dora Knight said, "I'm sorry your father has died. Fortunately, I haven't got a father to die." The boys always called her 'your smelly friend Dora Knight', which got abbreviated to 'S.F. friend'. I brought her home to tea once, but she was too shy to speak or eat and it wasn't a success, so she never came again.

The school had made arrangements to evacuate from London to a big house in Shropshire, but with war being averted by the Munich pact, the move was cancelled.

Dora said, "It was all so exciting. I was longing to go, but then it all came to nothing."

My mother sat in her bedroom, sometimes reading, sometimes looking out of the window; other times, just sitting. Mostly she just sat with Bristles on her lap. Being such a contrary cat, it was surprising that he obliged. Usually, if he knew you wanted something of him he would do the opposite. My mother had received a great number of sympathetic letters from all over the world. They all had to be acknowledged. Ian took it upon himself to answer them. He slaved away hour after hour, but by the time he went back to Cambridge for the autumn term, he still hadn't finished and took the remainder back with him to do there. That year he was lucky to have rooms in College. He was delighted not to be returning to Mrs. Warminger's green gloom and being faced by her heaving sea-sick-making bosom and disgusting little 'dainties' she was always cooking to please him.

After Ian had gone, my mother and I had to go through all my father's papers and belongings. A repetition of all the steps necessary after Granny Bell died.

We even had a bonfire of Daddy's most poignant things, but this time in our small London garden, overlooked as we were by the windows of the tall, painted Kensington houses. We hadn't realised what a lot of smoke there would be: it swirled round, hiding us from our neighbours and stinging our eyes. The fire smouldered and glowed well into the night and left a black mark on the grass like a savage scar.

Ruth was naturally very shaken by my father's death. She seemed to imagine that we were not as upset as we should have been, and the loss of 'Billiam' was not being mourned in an appropriate manner. She wrote:

'Dear Marion,

I have always felt that you and the family have never realised quite the importance of William's work and the esteem in which he was held worldwide. I only hope you do not suffer lasting regret at not having paid him the respect which I feel was his due. I have loved and admired him all my life, and now feel utterly bereft.

If I may make a suggestion about your future, I really do feel you would do well to sell your London house, especially as things appear so unsettled, and move down to Chapel House. I know there don't seem to be many young people in the neighbourhood for Hannah, but perhaps you could buy her a nag to ride about on, to keep her occupied.

Yours affectionately,
Ruth'

Her letter came as quite a shock to us, and my mother sent it on to Ian. He wrote to Ruth. I have no idea what he said, but he had a letter back from poor Arthur, which he showed to me when he came home. It said:

'Dear Boy,

Please tell your mother not to take Ruth's letter too much to heart. She has been so disturbed by your father's death. I'm sure that she would never knowingly hurt you all, in the way she seems to have done.

I hope you will be able to understand how it is. This must be a very difficult time for all of you.

If you need help with your fees, please let me know. It is the least that we could do. Your father did so much for us.
    Yours ever,
        Arthur'

We never saw Ruth again, although we did hear from her once or twice at Christmas time.

My father's Colonial Office pension died with him. All my mother was to get as his widow was a mere £200 a year. Her financial position was far from enviable.

Our solicitor, James Pendleton, was a kind young man. He made the necessary long discussions possible for us, especially for me. I found him so wonderfully good-looking and devastatingly attractive. After one of his visits, I ran upstairs and looked at myself in the glass from every angle. The more I looked, the more depressed I became. There didn't seem to be much point in going on living - I remember it vividly.

The boys and I decided to ignore Christmas altogether that year. In this way we would avoid an emotional crisis for our mother. Fritzi produced some Lebkuchen and four nasty little German angels. Apart from that we got away with it very lightly. David came home on Christmas Day, but left in the evening to be with friends. During the holiday, Ian and I walked the length and breadth of Kensington Gardens and Hyde Park. Once we persuaded our mother to join us. She made heavy weather of it and walked as though she were weighed down. I asked her if she felt better for the exercise, but she didn't answer. Perhaps she didn't hear.

The hurdle of Christmas over, it seemed necessary to 'address ourselves to the future', as Mr. Pendleton put it.

CHAPTER 19

Three main problems confronted us: money, of course; the car; and Chapel House.

"How can we stay at Stunford without transport?" my mother asked hopelessly. "I can't drive and Hannah's too young. Ian hasn't learnt yet and David has gone away. I suppose we shall have to get rid of the car anyway, because of the ghastly expense of garaging it in London."

We decided in the end to get David to drive it down to Stunford and put it in the shed by the back door.

"When Hannah is old enough," my mother continued, "she can learn to drive. Not that I ever want to see Chapel House again, but never mind."

The shortage of money loomed threateningly over us. In one of our talks with Mr. Pendleton, he made a suggestion. "To generate cash," he said, "why not turn the top floors of your house into flats? I have a friend who is an architect. I'll send him along to look at the layout, and if he sees possibilities, he can then make some drawings. I will explain to him that the conversion must be done with expense in mind and the minimal amount of work done. I'm sure his charge will be reasonable. He's a good chap - you'll like him." He had supper with us in the kitchen several times, and was keen about our house and the view from the top windows.

"So lovely to look over the trees of Ladbroke Square all the way to Richmond; anyone should love being here," he said. "You shouldn't have any trouble with letting."

When he ate with us, Fritzi made eyes at him all the time, which made us feel very uncomfortable.

* * * * *

We had a visit from the Borough Building Inspector. He upset my mother by being highly objectionable. So much so that she had to go to bed but, on the whole, everything went smoothly and work was quickly put in hand. All that was needed on both floors was a front door opening on to the stairs, and a boxed-in kitchenette. Once the workmen started, we felt horribly committed. We had to leave our bedrooms and move down, taking all our furniture with us. We had to clamber over tables and chairs to get into bed. The whole place looked like a sale room.

My mother had the drawing-room, I was in Arthur and Ruth's room, facing the street, and the boys were put together in what had been the dining-room, which we no longer used anyway.

It wasn't until Ian came home at Easter that things were sorted out. He piled all the surplus stuff into a room behind the kitchen in the basement.

Change is always disturbing. Bristles took it very hard.

Fritzi mildly larked with the workmen and pestered them with refreshments all the time - we were very embarrassed. "Poor thing," my mother remarked, "she knows no better, or perhaps she just can't help it."

Since David had joined the army, I had written to him religiously every week and he had written back. The time came when I realised suddenly that I was still sending my letters, but he had left off answering them. Very occasionally I got a postcard with a funny drawing on it, but no letters.

May wrote:

'My dear Marion,

I'm sorry that you didn't feel able to come to us for Christmas - I'm sure it would have helped, but never mind. We had a meeting at Marchfold the other day about the drawing-room floor. We didn't tell you about it because we thought you wouldn't want to be bothered at this time.

We were very lost without Will - he always stopped arguments and made important decisions for us.

We had a letter from Ian. He is a good boy. I hope you know how lucky you are.'

David drove the car down to Stunford and put it in the shed. He couldn't lock it up because the shed door was partly off its hinges. My mother had asked him to go into the house to see if all was well. He said it smelt very musty and shut up, but that the garden was full of flowers, if rather weedy. Mrs. Attwood came over whilst he was there. He thought she seemed rather sour. She asked him if we wanted her husband to dig the garden.

Later, he set off walking to Banbury to catch a train back to London, but was very fortunate and got a lift for more than half the way in a bread van. He brought with him a letter that he found lying on the front door mat, addressed to my mother. It was from the vicar of Stunford's wife, a Mrs. Havers:

'We were delighted to hear from our friend Ruth Colville that Chapel House is going to be occupied once more. Someone

Since David had joined the army, I had written to him religiously every week and he had written back. The time came when I realised suddenly that I was still sending my letters, but he had left off answering them. Very occasionally I got a postcard with a funny drawing on it, but no letters.

May wrote:

'My dear Marion,

I'm sorry that you didn't feel able to come to us for Christmas - I'm sure it would have helped, but never mind. We had a meeting at Marchfold the other day about the drawing-room floor. We didn't tell you about it because we thought you wouldn't want to be bothered at this time.

We were very lost without Will - he always stopped arguments and made important decisions for us.

We had a letter from Ian. He is a good boy. I hope you know how lucky you are.'

David drove the car down to Stunford and put it in the shed. He couldn't lock it up because the shed door was partly off its hinges. My mother had asked him to go into the house to see if all was well. He said it smelt very musty and shut up, but that the garden was full of flowers, if rather weedy. Mrs. Attwood came over whilst he was there. He thought she seemed rather sour. She asked him if we wanted her husband to dig the garden.

Later, he set off walking to Banbury to catch a train back to London, but was very fortunate and got a lift for more than half the way in a bread van. He brought with him a letter that he found lying on the front door mat, addressed to my mother. It was from the vicar of Stunford's wife, a Mrs. Havers:

'We were delighted to hear from our friend Ruth Colville that Chapel House is going to be occupied once more. Someone hair and does her face and feeds Bristles."

"The trouble is," Kate continued, "that your mother relied on your father for absolutely everything, and had no life of her own, and now she's paying the price. If you're not very careful Hannah, she'll batten on to you and hang on to you for the rest of her life and most of yours, and you'll never be able to go anywhere, or do anything, except be with her."

"Oh, I don't think so," I said. "After all, there are the boys."

"The boys," Kate exclaimed. "The boys! They will be gone and away any time now! You needn't count on them to keep her company."

Then she asked if I was going to school regularly. I had to admit that with all the turmoil, I had missed a lot.

"Does your mother write letters saying you're not well?"

"Sometimes she does," I admitted miserably.

We walked several times round the Square.

"We'd better go in," I said. "Mother will be wondering where we are."

The gardener was cutting the lawns. The sound of the mower, the smell of newly cut grass and the background noise of traffic, still encapsulate for me the feeling of living in London.

CHAPTER 21

David had some leave and came home. We had been expecting him at lunch time, but he didn't turn up until nearly 5. He drove up in a newly acquired very old car, with a girl. He introduced her to us as Violet. She was a charming, pretty girl and fitted into our family supper with unaffected ease. Afterwards, he took her home to South London and didn't get in again until well after midnight. We didn't see much of him during the week, but before returning to Barracks, he came into the schoolroom, drew up a chair, sat down beside my mother and said:

"Violet and I are going to get married."

There was a long pause, and then my mother turned to him and said, "You can't."

The obvious retort to those words is, "why not?", but David remained silent. My mother continued: "You can't be serious."

David still said nothing.

"What are you thinking of? You're in no position to marry - you own nothing, and you have no experience of life whatsoever. Have you asked your superior officers their permission? They'll never allow you to marry, and if you do so without their consent, they will ignore the existence of your bride. I've heard of that happening before in India, and how do you think you can live, both of you, on a subaltern's pay? I can't really think you've given this ridiculous idea any serious thought!"

After a pause, she started again. "This Violet girl, what's her background? Where do her people live, and who are they? What your father would say, I can't think - your army career could be ruined."

David remained entirely calm. Then he said, "Violet's father is a lay preacher."

My mother repeated the words, "lay preacher" as though it were a terrible disability or an appalling handicap.

"Lay preacher!" She said again, "lay preacher - how dreadful."

David laughed. "I'm afraid they are a very close and religious family."

"What about Violet?" my mother asked. "Is she the same?"

"It means a great deal to her too," David said. "When you get to know her, I'm sure she'll be as big a help to you as she has been to me."

That was where it was left. There didn't seem anymore to be said at that moment.

David went.

My mother put herself to bed.

Next day she said to me, "If your father were alive, this would never have happened. This girl certainly isn't out of the top drawer, although I have to say that she is pretty. I suppose David is a terrific catch."

A week later, David and Violet came again.

"Because you are so upset at the idea of us getting married, we've decided to postpone it, anyway, for the moment," Violet said. "After all, you've had a very sad time lately, so we don't want to worry you and make it worse." My mother was obviously deeply touched and relieved - her fears temporarily allayed.

Violet's mother and father came to see us. They arranged their visit by telephone and arrived exactly when they said they would. When Mrs. Waring came through the front door, she exclaimed, "Quite a mansion you've got here and look, marble floors!" (It was, in fact, a black and white composition floor and very difficult to keep clean.) I showed them into the schoolroom, where my mother was sitting. I brought tea up. We sat round and all was sipping and light, if a trifle artificial.

Both Violet's parents were short and rather fat. Their faces shone with a sort of pink blankness. After quite a long time of trivial conversation, a certain stressfullness seemed to take hold of them.

Mrs. Waring broke the ice by saying, "The reason we've come ... ", and then she hesitated, " ... is that your son David has asked Alfred if he can marry our daughter Violet. The trouble is, Mrs. Brocus, that we are not at all pleased at the idea. Alfred and I are devout churchgoers and try to lead our lives accordingly. The

Christian teaching is one of absolute love and in no way is retaliation or defence permissible. We are dedicated pacifists. The teaching in the Bible is crystal clear. There is no circumstance whatsoever in which the sword can be taken up, so you can see that the last thing we would want would be for our daughter to marry a man in the Army. If he became converted and left off being a soldier, of course, it would be another matter altogether. We've absolutely nothing against him personally, he's a nice lad. If there's a conscription, our son Stephen won't go. He's a conscientious objector and he'll go to jail for his beliefs, I know!"

My mother asked, rather flippantly, "But would he die for them, Mrs. Waring, and what about Onward Christian Soldiers?"

"That's just a manner of speaking," Mr. Waring said, dismissing her remark. "Anyway," he reminded her, "the hymn goes on 'marching AS to war."

Mrs. Waring had had her say, and was exhausted in her relief. Her husband patted her mottled hand reassuringly.

"For my part," my mother said coolly, "the whole idea of David marrying anybody at this time is absolute nonsense. For one thing, it would be totally unacceptable for a mere subaltern to marry. It would hinder his prospects hopelessly - any way, he's far too young."

The Warings were not particularly good listeners and their attention was already wandering.

My mother ploughed on, "I told them it was a ridiculous thing to do at their age, and they knew how worried and upset I was at the idea. A few days later, they came back and told us they had decided to postpone the wedding, for the time being anyway. I expect if we leave well alone, the whole thing will just fizzle out!"

The Warings seemed comforted and their anxiety abated somewhat, and they became less agitated.

"I'm so glad," Mr. Waring said, "that we both agree that this marriage would be unsuitable from every point of view."

"We do agree," my mother said emphatically. "Let's hope that we don't run into any difficulties.

All through the visit, Bristles had been tormenting poor Mr.

Waring. He wouldn't leave him alone. He jumped on his lap three times and padded on his knees. He rubbed against his trousers and purred and snagged one of his socks with an outstretched claw. At last Mrs. Waring said, "Albert is very sensitive to cats," so my mother put him out.

When the Warings left to go home, I walked with them to the tube station at Nottinghill Gate. Mr. Waring though short, had quite a vigorous strut. His wife took one and half strides to his two, which meant that she had to take an extra step every now and then to keep up. The effort made her a trifle breathless and as she lagged behind every now and then she missed what her husband had just said. Because of this, she was constantly gasping, "Pardon dear, what did you just say?"

As we walked down Kensington Park Road, Mrs. Waring said, "It's very sad for you and your mother that your father has died. You must feel the loss very much. What did he die of?"

I didn't answer because momentarily I was overwhelmed.

"Is it true that your brother is at Cambridge?"

"Yes," I said, "of course it's true, and David was there as well, but he left to join the Army."

Mr. Waring suddenly said, "Repentance, who has heard of that word nowadays?"

By this time we had reached the station - there we parted.

As they went towards the ticket office, I heard Mrs. Waring say, "I shall be home in plenty of time to put the potatoes on."

CHAPTER 22

Whenever Ian was at home, he spent all his time decorating the new flats. He worked endlessly. When they were completed, we got an agent to find tenants.

In no time at all, they were occupied - the top floor, by a young couple with a baby. Phillip and Rosemary Stafford was their name. Phillip worked at one of the big London shops and he was in the Territorials, which was why he was away such a lot of the time. His wife was devoted to him, and when they were together she never took her eyes off him. Sometimes, in the evening, they walked in the Square garden, pushing the baby in the pram. They always held hands. Whenever the Staffords were mentioned, my mother would say, "poor things, poor things," I can't think why. I thought how lucky they were to have each other.

In the floor below, there were two lady schoolteachers - Miss Armstrong and Miss Jones. Both of them were very good looking and young.

Although the flats were self-contained, our part of the house wasn't and our tenants had to walk up the stairs through the middle of our lives.

Miss Armstrong left a trail of scent behind her on the stairs when she and Miss Jones went out in the evening, which was often. Miss Armstrong had flowery floating dresses - Miss Jones wore suits.

Fritzi said she found Phillip Stafford very handsome, but the two young ladies she pronounced as "funny". In my ignorance, I had no idea what she meant, and when I had the chance, I looked closely at them to see if I could discover what constituted "funniness".

There was a pram parked permanently in the hall because of the Staffords' baby. Fritzi remarked that it lowered the tone of the house: "It's like a boarding house," she said.

The great upheaval in our lives meant our attention and thoughts had been very much centred on ourselves and our own affairs. After 'Munich', I think we hoped that there was nothing more to be worried about, in spite of the things David and some other people kept saying.

Then there was a new worry - my mother confided in me that she had noticed that Fritzi appeared to be pursuing Ian. "I suppose it's because she is German - Germans have strange morals. Many a German governess has corrupted her charges," she said. Whether she was or not, I don't know. I always loved Fritzi. To be with her was like being with someone of my own age. She certainly had drawbacks, like all her aches and pains and what the stars foretold, but that didn't really matter to me. My only other friend was smelly Dora Knight, who wasn't a friend at all, so when my mother told Fritzi that she must leave, it was a very sad day for me.

"Kindchen," she said, "I never thought your mother would turn me out. What will become of me now?" and she left, walking out into oblivion. I only hope the niece who was the famous opera singer looked after her, or that she got to the sister in Switzerland before war broke out. It was a long time before the pain of her departure abated for me, and thereafter I lacked companionship cruelly.

May Week came at Cambridge. I longed for a chance to go, but, of course, I was far too young and, anyway, it would have been out of the question in the circumstances.

Ian brought a girl home several times. She was quite nice, but very intense and political and had a lot of boyish mannerisms. She seemed always to have a rucksack on her back, which usually appeared to be empty. She gave the impression of just having come back from a hike. I believe that she did do a lot of walking. She described to us how she had followed the footsteps of Wordsworth and his sister Dorothy in the Lake District. She had also followed the footsteps of Coleridge both there and in other places.

Ian got a holiday job on a farm in Suffolk. He wrote to us saying how much he was enjoying himself.

There started to be a crisis between Hitler and the Poles over Danzig. Then the Germans made a pact with the Russians. "The forces of evil have joined together against the world," everybody said. "Now we know where we stand. Hitler and his henchmen and Stalin and his murderers are plotting to destroy the world." Meanwhile, in our bit of space, life went on much as it had done since my father's death. But with Fritzi gone and nobody left to cook or arrange matters, I soon realised that I was the one who had got to see to our affairs, buy food and feed whoever happened to be at home.

My mother said, "Hannah, you look worn out, would you like it if we went down to Stunford for a few days to see how we get on? Before I felt as though I couldn't bear even to see the place, but now I feel as though I could manage it."

I didn't particularly want to go, but I thought I'd better say, "yes, it would be nice." It was arranged for the Staffords to feed Bristles and shut him safely in the schoolroom at night. They were very willing, even enthusiastic about it.

CHAPTER 23

We took a train from Paddington to Banbury. The atmosphere everywhere was extraordinary because of the heightening crisis: a sort of brittle hysteria gripped the country. A dreadful tense excitement could be felt. In the train the passengers were overfriendly and chatted in an abnormal way. From the windows of the train we watched the harvest fields speed by. A man in our compartment said, "They start wars when the harvest's in, they always have."

A thin woman, who had been telling us all the details of an operation she had just had, agreed with him. "I suppose so," she said in a vague, uninterested voice.

After arriving at Banbury Station, we got a taxi to take us to Chapel House.

Entering the house was not unlike diving into icy water - it was cold, it was damp, it was empty. We hadn't been there for well over a year. I opened the windows, and the doors, letting the last gasp of summer flood in.

The apple tree was loaded with huge apples. The branches weighed down to the ground.

While we were there my mother sat at the open door of the so-called sun-room. She even wandered into the garden and pulled up a few weeds. I asked her if she thought she could get interested in gardening, like Granny Bell. "I don't know," she said, "I suppose, I might." Nevertheless, towards the end of our short visit, she suddenly said, "Hannah, I feel better. I never thought I would, but I do. This is a lovely place, even if the house is a bit pokey."

Mrs. Attwood came every day to tidy up. She chatted to my mother though, most of the time. One morning, she came to tell us that we had to go the village school to be fitted with gas masks.

The school was about three-quarters of a mile away. There was a steady stream of people going that way. In those days, people lived where they worked. Most of them had been born in the village and seldom went outside it. They looked at strangers with great mistrust and even hostility. As we walked along, everyone stared at us, many turned round to look. Nobody spoke.

At the school a couple of ladies were fitting the gas masks. There were three sizes: large, medium and a complete 'bag' for babies and small children. When I saw my mother in her 'medium', I burst out laughing. She looked like a huge insect. No size fitted me. 'Small' wouldn't accommodate my nose and because my face was so thin, 'medium' hung limply off my cheeks, instead of fitting snugly and blubbering when I breathed out, as it should have done. I was given the 'medium' because there was no alternative.

We each walked away with our gas masks in cardboard boxes hung across our shoulders with string. The instructions were to carry them with us at all times.

We had a visit from one of the Miss Bates. Ruth had mentioned them in her letter, describing them as being highly intellectual and interesting. When I opened the door, she seemed rather taken aback. "Is your mother or father in?" she asked. She was a large woman with a shock of wiry white hair. She wore a thick tweed skirt and on her long feet, strong shoes.

I invited her in, and called my mother. When they met, she said, "I'm Frances Bates. Ruth Colville wrote telling us that you had taken Pamela Moreton's house. We hope very much that you are a serious gardener because it would be sad to think of her garden being neglected. It's a great responsibility for you. She was a lifelong friend of ours, and we miss her very much."

My mother didn't answer.

Miss Bates continued, "The news is so shocking, we hardly know whether we are coming or going. I expect you feel the same - we never thought we'd have to face this again."

She then walked past my mother and went to the new sitting-room and looked through the glass door. We followed her.

"It looks pretty derelict to me," she said, and then went on, "I'm really here because I have to find places for evacuees to stay. They've made me billeting officer. I've put you down for a mother and three children."

My mother told her that we were going back to London the next day.

"I'm afraid I shall have to put them in your house, whether you're here or not," she replied rather sharply.

Strangely they never came, and we didn't hear any more about it. A year later we had a sweet little girl, but she didn't stay long because of what happened. This was our first real experience of Chapel House and Stunford. After this visit we felt as though we lived there. Just before we left, we heard on the wireless that the Germans and the Russians had invaded Poland.

CHAPTER 24

We left Stunford in the village taxi, driven by Mr. Cox, a thin little man who had a recovered-invalid wife, "little Miss Miracle". He told us the whole story on the way to Banbury Station. How she had lain on a water bed for nine months and only sipped honey and water and egg white. He never referred to the world crisis and didn't seem to take much interest in what was happening. We came to know Mrs. Cox remotely later on, when we called to book the taxi. She had a strange resemblance to a hot water bottle, but it may have been confused in my mind with the water bed.

The train from Banbury was full of soldiers. Paddington was crammed with servicemen. The atmosphere was electric. No one could believe it was happening. Relentlessly events swept on. We were all helpless spectators.

When we got home, we were relieved to find Bristles happily asleep in the schoolroom. We found Phillip's wife pale and tearful - he had been called up.

"Phillip doesn't want me to stay here alone with baby because of the air raids," she said. "I'm going to pack up tomorrow and go down to my parents in Hampshire."

'Tomorrow' was the day that the Germans and Russians invaded Poland. The Poles defended their country with cavalry - pathetic gallantry against the mass of ruthless tanks smashing into them. Two days later, we were at war. Half-an-hour after the declaration, the air raid sirens went, but nothing happened.

We were told that there was to be a complete blackout. No lights to show whatever after dark. Fortunately, in London we had shutters and thick curtains at most of the windows, but not in the basement. I was very lucky to find a little shop that still had some black material, as almost everywhere was sold out. We covered the kitchen windows with it and secured it with drawing pins. While we were thus occupied, we heard a motorbicycle stop. It was Ian. We were so glad to see him. He looked amazingly brown and handsome from working on the farm. He said that he wanted to go into the

Airforce as soon as he could. He had bought the motorbicycle for £10 from one of the farm labourers.

The purpose of his visit was to tell us that he thought we should leave London at once and go down to Chapel House and stay there until the war was over. "There may be air raids at any time," he said.

Later, he took me aside and, looking hard into my face, said, "Hannah, I want you to promise me that, with David and me away, you will stay with Mother whatever happens. You mustn't go off doing war work or anything like that. You must stay with her - promise?"

"Alright, I promise," I replied.

He left early in the morning.

A letter came from my school, saying that they were evacuating down to Devon. They gave a day and time for me to join the school, travelling from Paddington Station. I couldn't go, of course, because of my promise. Anyway, I didn't want to go, so that was the last of my schooling.

Just beyond our garden, flying above the Square, was a huge grey barrage balloon. It was tethered to a lorry. In charge of it was a man in Airforce uniform. He told us that its purpose was to deter German planes from flying low. My mother said, "How reassuring."

Miss Armstrong and Miss Jones came down to talk to us. They were both going to the country with their school, but said they wanted to keep the flat because, as soon as they could, they intended to come back to London to join one of the Civil Defence services. Miss Armstrong appeared to be very brittle and tense, but Miss Jones was very protective and bossy.

Our wireless went wrong. I had to go and buy another so that we could listen to every news. I also bought two torches in case we had to go out in the darkened street for any reason - perhaps to look for Bristles, if he didn't come in.

One evening, the front doorbell rang. I was in the kitchen cooking supper and ran up. I opened the door and there stood David and Violet. David looked so smart and splendid in his uniform. Violet was more beautiful than I remembered. I felt a pang of jealousy

I'm afraid. My mother was overjoyed to see David, but not so pleased to see Violet, who she hoped had fallen by the wayside during the world upheavals, declarations of war and pressure from the pacifist parents.

At once the atmosphere was uneasy. We all went into the kitchen. David took my mother's hand and said, "Mother, Violet and I are married." My mother made a strange reply, "So I see," she said. Perhaps she had seen the ring on Violet's hand. I said, "have you told Ian?"

We had a tense supper. It was almost as though we had suddenly become strangers. None of us had anything to say. There was nothing to say.

They didn't stay long. I saw them off into the black street. I gave David one of the torches I had bought. I stood outside listening to them walking away in the darkness. I heard Violet trip and stumble a little with her high heels. By the time I had come in and shut the front door, my mother was in bed.

Next day, I telephoned the Aunts to tell them that David was married. My mother told me to keep the calls short because of the expense. It was difficult because they wanted to be indignant at great length, and were curious (of course) to know what Violet was like and what sort of family she came from. I didn't tell them that her father was a lay preacher. I wasn't quite sure what it was anyway, except to remember that my mother thought it was dreadful. That it was something to do with the church and preaching, I knew, but why she was so shocked I did not understand.

All the time we were anxious about what would happen next. Every night we expected there would be an air raid, but gradually we started to get accustomed to the threat.

Two government information leaflets were published. Leaflet No. 1 instructed us to carry a luggage label with us at all times and on it should be written our names and addresses. Leaflet No. 2 told us to paint round our windows with black paint, to ensure no chink of light was visible round the edge of the blackout curtains. Even a spot of light brought about a rumpus and a fine. A national register was being compiled, and food rationing was being organised, drawing on past experiences and mistakes of the First World War.

What we, fortunately, did not know at the time, was that the government was expecting 100,000 casualties during the early weeks of the war. Hospitals had been cleared, mortuaries supplied with stacks of cardboard coffins and lime-pits dug to deal with the dead.

Every household was given a stirrup-pump and a long-handled shovel to deal with incendiary bombs.

There was some talk of the war being over by Christmas. Perhaps we thought it would end before it had really begun, but it had started in earnest at sea. The loss of ships and men were daily broadcast. The enemy, they told us, was intent on starving us out. The battleship, The Royal Oak, was sunk by a U-boat at her base at Scapa Flow, together with 800 of her crew.

The war years were a span of time cut entirely out of my life. I only started to live again when it ended. It was a time full of fear, sadness, frustration and unspeakable boredom. I didn't really believe it would ever end. I thought the whole of my life was going to be spent in that way.

Writing about those years now, I find there is little to write about. The days were days to get through somehow. Endurance and stress were only punctuated by shocking and painful events. Of actual privation, there was none to speak of, just continual anxiety.

After the war when I was with my contemporaries, I was amazed to learn that for many of them the war had been the highlight of their lives. Their time in the Forces or doing war work had been so exciting, and the companionship so diverting, that their subsequent lives seemed dull and meaningless by comparison and their after-the-war relationships endlessly unsatisfactory.

Of all sections of the community to suffer most, I think, were the young married women, left behind with small children to look after. Their husbands away fighting in various parts of the world, they lived continually with the dread of bad news from the battlefronts, striving alone, as they had to, with the deadly chores of lonely and frustrating housekeeping. At night, when the children were in bed and the blackout curtains drawn, the evenings must have stretched into eternity, without mentioning the longing.

Christmas came. It was still 1939. The war wasn't over after all. My mother said, "Why does it always have to be Christmas?"

I had had my seventeenth birthday.

Ian was with us in London. He gave me a diary. I wrote in it nearly every day. Looking through it now, I see I recorded events mostly heard on the wireless, interspersed with trivial happenings.

Ian was very impatient that we hadn't moved out of London as he had suggested, and set about packing us up at once for the move. A cat basket was bought for Bristles and we made the journey down to Stunford by train.

As soon as we arrived there, he got the car out of the garage and made it go. Then he taught me to drive. I had no difficulty in learning and was soon completely proficient, or so I thought. My mother complained that I drove rather fast. There were hardly any other cars on the roads at that time - I never hit a tree or a telegraph pole and never went into a ditch, so I suppose it was alright.

In spite of the ground being icy, I was able to take Ian to Banbury Station when he left. It was an exciting experience to be able to drive, but I felt very forlorn as the train drew out of the station and disappeared down the line.

CHAPTER 25

We kept Bristles in for several days and buttered his paws, which kept him occupied.

For a London cat to find himself in the middle of the country, with nothing going on, must have been a horrible shock, but he soon adjusted to his new surroundings and seemed to enjoy life again.

My mother constantly bemoaned the fact that we had taken Chapel House instead of finding somewhere in Sussex.

There was a foot of snow on the ground. Even before Ian left, it had started to be very cold. A few weeks later, nobody could get through to Banbury - the drifts were over the hedges. All our windows at Chapel House were covered with swirling patterns of frost flowers. They only melted during the day in the kitchen where there was a fire alight. Things were difficult from the outset.

The Russians had attacked Finland; the fire smoked in the kitchen; we had no hot water because there was no fuel for the boiler, but we did have an electric kettle. We hadn't heard from David; food rationing came in and we were issued with ration books.

We had to register at the village shop for butter or margarine, sugar and bacon - at the same village shop that we had walked to with my father a year or more before. I hadn't been back there since. It seemed an ordeal for me to go in with the ration books, but it was no good putting it off.

As I pushed the door open, the bell on the door clanged. The few customers that were in there stopped talking and turned round and stared - it seemed forever.

Inside the shop it was a dim twilight, being lit only by the reflected evening glow from the snow outside.

After a few seconds of intense glowering, everyone turned away and continued their business. My turn came to be served and I produced our ration books to register. In the meantime, other people had come in. It was obvious they found me interesting. They gazed at me without stopping.

This was my first encounter with Mrs. Farley on my own.

She was a very intimidating presence. As the war progressed and goods became scarcer, her power increased. If you fell foul of her in any slight degree, you lost all chance of having a share of the things off the ration book which were kept under the counter. I tried hard, and somehow succeeded in remaining a constant favourite. Sometimes I used to look at her pale savage face, wondering what would become of her when the war ended (if it ever did) and she no longer had power to decide who should and who should not have lavatory paper and bananas.

There was a Mr. Farley, who lurked in the back shadows amongst the string and mousetraps. He hardly ever spoke, although he was required sometimes to cut coupons out of ration books. He was never permitted to slice the bacon on the machine. I'm sure he longed for a turn but was never allowed. He used to step forward, as if to seize the controls, but was immediately pushed aside.

They had a dreary, mud-coloured daughter called Joan, who stood behind the counter sometimes. Mrs. Farley always hinted that she suffered from an internal disorder of some kind, and further spoke of having bought the shop as "something for Joan to do," as though she were handicapped, but I suspected that they meant to hold her captive, so that she would never meet young men and want to get married. In this ploy they failed. I heard that after the war she married an American and went to live in some far-off place in the Mid-West that no one has ever heard of, not even Americans.

CHAPTER 26

While Ian was with us, he had arranged for us to be put on the telephone (we never ever got it!), and he also bought three oil stoves: one for the hall, one for my mother's bedroom and one for mine. We found a man who delivered paraffin once a month. As time went by, I learnt all the skills of daily wick-trimming and oil heater craft - the flame should burn evenly, and blue and yellow spikes meant trouble. The horror of a smoking oil stove has to be experienced, it can't be imagined. A whole room or house can be blackened an inch-deep in oil-soaked soot and the air so thickened with smoke that you can't see the walls. The comfort they brought us was immense. I lit them in wintertime every night when it got dark, after drawing the blackout curtains. In bed, in the dark I used to lie and watch the shimmering pattern cast on the ceiling by the perforated top.

A piece of paper was pushed through our letterbox. At the top was written 'Knitting for Victory' and below it stated that 'A Knitting Party will be held at The Croft at 3pm on January 28 - Basic specifications for sea-boot stockings and balaclava helmets are available, but not detailed patterns. Wool and needles will be supplied.' It was signed 'Edna Hunter'.

The Croft was only a short distance away. We had seen the name many times as we walked past.

My mother said, "We must try to join in, and anyway it's important to get to know our neighbours."

When the day came, we went.

The Croft was a stone house of three stories. It had obviously been a farmhouse. Beside it was a group of semi-rural barns and outhouses around a yard. A governess cart was tilted, the shafts on the ground, under a lean-to roof. Snow covered everything, showing clearly the different angles of the buildings.

The front door was opened by its owner, a tall thin woman with her iron-grey hair done strictly in a bun. She didn't seem very welcoming. We were shown into the sitting-room, where a number

111

of women were sitting knitting. They all stopped and looked up.

"This is our new neighbour from Chapel House and her daughter. Tell us your name," she asked coldly.

"Brocus," my mother replied in a low voice.

"Mrs. Brocus," our hostess announced.

We were given wool and needles and started off knitting scarves, having declared our lack of skill.

The room was cold - it had a specific 'front parlour' smell. A mixture of damp and rectitude. Everyone's breath was faintly visible. It mingled between us, like a mist going up from the face of the earth.

The women chatted a little amongst themselves. My mother made one or two remarks, which got no response, and then lapsed into silence.

It was obvious there that everyone came from a certain layer of village society. It was also apparent that they didn't wish to be too friendly to us in case we proved later to be unsuitable acquaintances.

There was a large black cat sitting right beside the hearth close to some smouldering embers in the grate. The moment I saw him, I was afraid he was a fighter and that he meant trouble for Bristles, and so he proved to be. He was a catcher of birds and altogether a criminal class cat of the lowest sort.

When the time came to go home, we left thankfully, carrying our knitting with us.

We never went again. it was snowing outside. I'm afraid my scarf didn't get any further. I found it years later in the back of a drawer, when we were packing up to leave Chapel House.

Next day when Mrs. Attwood was tidying up, my mother asked her about Mrs. Hunter at The Croft. "O 'er, miserable thing she is," she replied.

Mr. Havers, the vicar, and his wife called. I remembered what Aunt Ruth had said about them in her letter and we were interested to see them. Any diversion was welcome.

It was evening when they came. They introduced themselves and stamped the snow off their boots as they stepped into the hall.

Mr. Havers said in a low voice, "we were very sorry to hear about your father." I invited them into the kitchen and offered them tea. My mother joined us from her bedroom. They sat down in front of the fire, at the same time protesting that they could only stay a few minutes.

Mrs. Havers said, "we have come to invite you to the Vicarage for tea. I had a letter from Ruth Colville." She looked at my mother, "I believe she is your sister-in-law. I promised her that we would call on you. I'm afraid our visit has been rather delayed. We did come some time ago, but you weren't in. Ruth had a very nasty accident in Germany, didn't she and, although she has written, we haven't seen her since."

The Vicar was silent. He gave the impression that he was very pre-occupied. He had a walking stick and wrote patterns with it on the stone floor. The only thing he said was, "I see you have a cat."

Poor Mrs. Havers obviously tried to relieve the awkwardness of her husband's gloomy manner. She was fidgety, nervous and everlastingly apologetic. In appearance and in her clothes she gave the impression of falling to pieces. I suppose it was her extreme agitation that caused everything about her to shift.

It was arranged that we go to the Vicarage the next Wednesday. "Come about 4 o'clock," Mrs. Havers suggested, "then you'll only have to walk in the dark one way!"

As they were leaving, Mrs. Havers asked me where I went to school. Then she said, "I heard that you went to the knitting party at Mrs. Hunters. Mrs. Chauter, who has come to live at Barrymore, just below the Vicarage, told me she very much regretted not having spoken to you, but didn't know at the time who you were." Mrs. Havers continued, "we're so encouraged to have such nice new people as the Chauters in the village. They have quite a passable collection of china."

After they'd left I asked my mother what a passable collection of china was. "I suppose," my mother said, "she means cups and saucers and plates like the ones Granny had at Marchfold."

The Aunts wrote letters to my mother. They were full of

hidden tension. Most of our cousins were too young to be called up, but if the war didn't come to an end soon, they would all be going. Uncle James was a territorial, so he had gone and so had Evelyn's husband.

'If you should feel like going to look at Marchfold - don't. It is absolutely desolate. I can't think what's going to happen to it now. Aren't you worried about the London house? I expect you've heard that poor May is moving. Harold is taking over a factory in Coventry, and they've rented a house in the nearby village of Altrington. Have you got over the shock yet of David getting married without telling you? Do you realise that none of us has even seen her yet?'

"It'll be nice to have May not too far away," my mother said. "It can't be more than thirty miles to Coventry from here. We'll be able to drive over and see her, if we've got any petrol."

From my Diary, 9th Feb:
- *The Thames is frozen over for eight miles, as is the sea at Bognor. They say it's the coldest weather this century.*

The evacuees are returning to the cities. They don't see the point of being in the country away from home if there aren't going to be any air raids. We are thinking of going back to London ourselves. Mother is worried all the time about David. She says she will feel better when we get the telephone.

Tomorrow we go out to tea at the Vicarage. I am not looking forward to it.

CHAPTER 27

The walk to the Vicarage took us the full length of our side of the village. The snow was golden-pink in the last rays of the sun. A flock of birds were settling to roost in a small tree beside the road: they looked like leaves. As we came near, they bounced off into the air leaving the branches bare. My mother said they must have been finches of some sort. The sky was completely clear. Although homely smoke was rising from the cottage chimneys, no lights were showing in any of the windows because of the blackout. As we went along, the snow squeaked beneath our boots. It was freezing hard. We passed several muffled up people scurrying along. We came to the village school, where we had got our gas-masks months before, then over the crossroads and beyond to the frozen pond in front of the Vicarage.

We rang the doorbell and waited. The vicar opened it and we stepped inside. We had thought our house was cold, but in comparison to this, it was almost warm.

"I'm afraid the hall is rather cold," he said. "I had meant to light the paraffin stove earlier because of your coming, but I forgot."

Mrs. Havers appeared. The buttons of her cardigan were done up wrongly. "Come in you poor things," she said, "and get warm. We've got a good fire in the sitting-room. Would you like to take your things off or keep them on for a while?"

She led the way down a passage.

"This vicarage is the most rambling and inconvenient place that ever was," she mumbled as we followed her.

Their sitting-room was a comfortable cluttered place. The walls were covered with books. The curtains had not been drawn and the windows looked down the walled garden and in the fading light one could just make out the shrubs and plants which were humped over and huddled into rounded shapes by the snow.

Mrs. Havers drew the curtains, saying as she did so, "I should have drawn them before, I know. I can't get used to the blackout."

A huge fire was burning in the hearth. In front of it on the rug was the most appalling-looking dog. He was lying on his back, his pink underside and exposed parts gave off a strong smell of scorching.

Mrs. Havers went up to him as though reading my thoughts. "Gillie," she said, giving him a little push onto his side, "let's make you a little more presentable. I'm afraid poor Gillie has got rather old."

My mother was given a rather beautiful carved chair to sit on. It had a threadbare black brocade seat. I sat on the sofa with Mrs. Havers. She pointed out that some of the springs were broken. " ... but if we have it mended, it won't be nearly as comfortable as it is now!" Mr. Havers took a stool and sat back from the blaze. "I find the fire rather hot," he said. He was certainly right, it was overpowering, especially after the intense cold outside. I started peeling off my clothes, and so did my mother. As layer after layer was discarded, I felt we became more and more vulnerable and at a disadvantage. I looked at my mother in her remaining Shetland jumper, fat and sloppy in parts, and thought how ghastly she looked. Her face had gone red with the heat and the cold, and so had mine.

"Have you suffered from any frozen pipes?" Mrs. Havers enquired. "Our outside tap is solid, but so far we've been lucky. It's when the thaw comes that the damage becomes apparent!"

After talking for a short while, Mr. Haver said, "Tea wouldn't come amiss, dear."

Mrs. Havers got up.

After she had left the room, Mr. Havers pulled his stool up. (The fire had subsided a little.) "Mrs. Brocus," he said, "how do you find the village? I heard that you were in Sussex before, is that right?"

My mother replied that we had been here such a short time that it was impossible to make any real judgement.

"It's a funny sort of place," he continued, "split into more factions than most communities. There are a great number of Quakers, said to have settled here after the Civil War. They have intermarried continually and are very inbred. There's a lot of mental trouble amongst them, in spite of their noble features. They are, of course, pacifists and some of them have been taken from here and interned on The Isle of Man for preaching sedition. Have you seen the Meeting House? Such a dreary damp-looking building. Then there are the Methodists and, of course, my church. I have adversaries there too, in the Misses Turner, who keep the Post Office. They are very Low Church.

A very flamboyant actor lived in the village at one time. He it was that built that place that looks like a folly at the crossroads. He gave the church a very nice embroidered piece to hang behind the Altar. It covered a great lump of stone with the ten commandments carved on it. The Misses Turner said it was tantamount to blasphemy to cover such holy words. They said they had known them all their lives and when you went up to the Altar, it was salutary to be reminded of God's Law, and they never face the east during the creed. They complain endlessly about heathen practices. On the whole, I'm afraid I have to say that Stunford is not the kindest of places. The people are not friendly and some of them are fairly vicious, not only to new comers, but amongst themselves. We have been here a long time now."

Mrs. Havers brought in the tea. She had to go back and fetch the scones and again for the sugar and jam. Each time she opened the door a wonderful gulp of cold air came in. I remember that the scones were delicious, and so was the strawberry jam. It was home-made from strawberries out of the garden, Mrs. Havers told us.

Mr. Havers sat on his stool, eating scones and dropping crumbs on his knees - some got lodged on his stomach. "I hear," he said, "that the Russians have launched a fresh attack on Finland. It looks as though the Fins are more than holding their own. There is talk of us sending an expeditionary force."

Immediately, I knew my mother was thinking David might be sent.

The dog was roused from sleep by the sound of eating and waddled over trying to look appealing.

"You know you're too fat already," Mrs. Havers said indulgently, and gave him a scone.

Presently, the Vicar got up, brushed the crumbs off his trousers and said, "I've got some important letters to get off, I know you'll excuse me if I go and get on with them." As he was leaving, he turned and said to my mother, "shall we be seeing you in church, Mrs. Brocus?"

My mother was rather taken aback. "I expect so," she answered rather feebly, "sometimes."

As he left the room, Mrs. Havers called after him, "The study is so cold dear, put your overcoat on and light the stove - do!"

Mrs. Havers explained that her husband was inclined to bronchitis in wintertime and shouldn't really put himself at risk by going from one extreme of temperature to another.

Beside the sofa was a table. Standing on it were a great number of family photographs. Mrs. Havers stretched over and picked up a picture of a young man. She handed it to my mother.

"That is my son, Andrew," she said. "I have a daughter too. She got married about a year ago. She lives in Nottingham. Her husband works in the family firm. He's been called up. She is expecting a baby. I've asked her if she'd like to come and live with us for the time being. She says she hasn't made up her mind yet."

"Andrew is waiting to go into the RAF. He's full of excitement and enthusiasm about it. I find it very hard to hide my feelings." My mother told her about David and Ian.

Mrs. Havers' hair kept coming undone and she continually tried to keep it up by resticking her hairpins into it.

We stayed ages, or so it seemed to me. At last we made a move to leave. As we were going, Mrs. Havers put her hand on my mother's arm, and said very gently, "I didn't like to mention it before, but I did know that you have had a very sad time."

Walking home under the stars, I was stricken with grief about my father; we were really and truly adrift.

As I was getting breakfast next morning, the post came. I saw at once that there was a letter from David. I took it straight to my mother. Her face lit up. This is what it said:

'My dear Mother,
I know you will be thrilled to hear that Violet is going to

have a baby. I didn't tell you before, because I thought you might be worried with everything being so uncertain.

Of course, we are absolutely delighted. As you know, Violet is still staying with her parents. I wasn't too happy about it because of the air raids, but as there haven't been any, it's turned out alright.

We're training hard. Violet sends her love.

Love to Hannah.

> *David'*

My mother remarked that it was strange that he hadn't told us when the baby was due.

Two days after our visit to the Vicarage Mrs. Havers walked over to see us. We were surprised to have a visitor. She brought the dog, so I quickly shut Bristles in my mother's bedroom.

"I felt I must come," she said, "I'm sure we have so much in common. Things aren't easy for me either, and we've both got sons to worry about. I know you are waiting for the telephone to be put in; until it's connected do give our number to your family to ring if they want to get in touch with you. If you want to telephone to them, please don't hesitate to come to the Vicarage. At the Post Office everyone can hear what you're saying and, although it may not be anything of importance, it is very inhibiting; and, besides, one doesn't want one's business relayed all round the village. I can't stay long. Gillie is so slow walking these days and Charles will wonder where I've got to."

In spite of what she said, she didn't seem to be in any hurry to go. She confided in my mother that her husband was a very disappointed man. Preferment had never come his way. He had not expected to spend all his days in an out-of-the-way country parish, but felt that he had been destined for higher things. "It seems such a waste," she added, "that a classical scholar of such brilliance shouldn't use his talents for the benefit of the Church at large."

CHAPTER 28

It was about this time that we started going to London. We left poor Bristles shut up with a cat tray and Mrs. Attwood to feed him. These journeys to and fro by village taxi and then train, were called, "seeing if the house was still alright." London was sadly changed - shabby and mostly deserted. A lot of the houses in our road were empty. Mrs. Gridling from down the road came in to see us. "So you're back," she observed, "I'll put you on the fire-watching rota and get you tin hats."

Our lady tenants were in great form - smart in their tight new uniforms and thick make-up. They greeted us in a very reserved sort of way, as though they resented us returning to the house at all. Perhaps they liked to think of it as theirs.

The gas pressure was very low for some reason, so our fires didn't give out much heat and we were very cold. Everything had got sticky with grime while we had been away and I set to work to clean up as best I could.

One evening while we were huddled in the dim light of the basement over some scrambled eggs, we had a visit from Francis Morley, the young man who had helped us to do the flats. I hardly recognised him. He had joined the ranks of an Infantry Regiment, and was now an officer cadet. After so much physical training, he was transformed from an absolute weed into a man. I cooked him a scrambled egg and he ate a lot of bread with it. He was on leave.

He asked my mother if he could take me out to the cinema next day, and she said, "Of course, as long as you're not late bringing her back!" I didn't want to leave her alone, but she insisted. He turned up at the appointed time with a box of chocolates, and took my hand. After the film we went to a little restaurant and had beans on toast, and then he took me home. I really enjoyed the outing.

My mother was in bed when I got back. It was barely ten o'clock. As Francis was going, he said, "I'll write to you, Hannah," which he did for some time. I never bothered to answer any of his letters. I'm ashamed to say that I didn't even read many of them, but threw them away unopened. In the end, he left off writing. I have no idea what happened to him.

CHAPTER 29

When we got back to Stunford that time, my mother said a very dangerous thing. She said, "I suppose we are now really displaced people; we don't belong anywhere anymore." She didn't know what she was talking about. It is very unwise, or so I felt, to say things like that when you've still got everything.

Bristles wouldn't go out because the black cat that I had seen at the knitting party was terrorising him.

Miss Bates came, The Miss Frances Bates who had tried to make us have evacuees. This time she wanted us to contribute to an organisation engaged in trying to get Jews out of Germany. "The release has just been obtained," she told us, "of a most distinguished Doctor and his wife from Vienna. They arrived in this country last week and have now come to stay with us here. They are going to live in England until their papers are in order to leave for America."

She invited us to meet them, and a few days later we went. There we became acquainted with her sister, Mary. It was the first time we had been to their house. It was rather a gaunt place, built of stone with three storeys: a covering of snow made it look even bleaker. Inside, it was far from warm, but the rooms were large and elegant and there were books everywhere. Miss Mary was smaller and softer altogether than her big, vigorous sister.

We were shown into the drawing-room and introduced to the Doctor and his wife. Both of them were short, but they had become thin. Dr. Scharf had a shiny bald head and Mrs. Scharf had thick spectacles and greasy hair. She was wearing a grey-pink jumper with a knitted flower on the front. All the time she stayed at Stunford, she wore it. I remember blaming her for looking as she did. If you made yourself look like that, I thought, no wonder you got treated badly, but of course I didn't realise she had nothing else to wear.

They said very little, but spoke very adequate English. It wasn't until years later that I really took in what had happened to them.

Vienna had been their home. They had lived there all their

lives in prosperity and comfort, surrounded by a wide circle of friends and happy with their neighbours. Both of them had successful careers, especially the Herr Doctor, who was considered brilliant in his field. Then the Anschluss came. "Overnight everything was changed." Their non-Jewish friends shunned them, their neighbours became hostile - things went from bad to worse. They were subjected to every indignity imaginable. Persecuted, restricted and ill-treated, the Doctor was arrested by the Gestapo. When he was released after endless beatings, his face was so swollen and battered he was unrecognisable.

By leaving Austria and going to America, they intended to establish a haven for their family, who they hoped would be able to escape from the Fascist grasp and join them. This never happened. Their loved ones perished in the most brutal ways. Mrs. Scharf's mother was taken and pushed alive into the steam chamber of a laundry and scalded to death. Her sister was made, with others, to climb the wall bars of a gymnasium. There they had to stay clinging on near the ceiling until exhaustion made them try to come down. Beatings with whips forced them to climb up again, until at last, all strength gone, they fell to the floor and death. Fortunately, the Scharfs didn't know about these horrors as they sat on the Misses Bates' chairs, talking about the weather and the treacherous condition of the roads.

The word 'refugee' was a word often heard at that time. It didn't mean anything much to me, but seeing the Scharfs brought it into focus. An undercurrent of terror was so strong beneath their normalness, partly because it was blurred and speechless. I dreamt that I was looking down on a concentration camp: the chained prisoners were sitting on concrete steps round a pit. As I flew over (which is what I seemed to be doing) they looked at me in dumb silence. I can see it now, the squalor and ugliness of it was shocking; the confined intensity of fear oppressive.

From my Diary:
My mother listens to the news every hour, on the hour. The news is all bad. The Germans are building more U-boats

than we are sinking; the blockade is threatening all our food.
We seem to be coping with magnetic mines, by some invention.
Neutral ships coming in our direction are now being sunk.

CHAPTER 30

Today Ian turned up. He came in a taxi, with all his things. he is going to stay here until he gets his call-up papers. I was glad to see him. We laughed and laughed all about nothing while we made up his bed and stacked his things away.

The Finns have had to give in to the Russians.

16th March:

I heard the cuckoo.

With Ian here everything seems different. he works all day getting everything straight and making it work. He longs to start digging in the garden, but, the ground is far too wet. We've decided to dig up all the plants and put vegetables in as soon as it dries out enough. But Ian will almost certainly have gone by then.

Meat rationing has started. We're not going to get much at all. If it's just mother and me we shall have to save up coupons and get some once a month.

I remember how restless Ian was. I dreaded him leaving, but the day dawned when the envelope came through the letterbox and lay on the doormat. It was an inevitable blow.

He had to report to a camp in the north-east. He was obviously thrilled to be off and when I took him to the station, I saw how light his step was as he walked along the platform.

All the time Ian was with us, Mrs. Attwood doted on him: I found it very irritating.

Time went by. The Germans attacked Denmark and then Norway. My mother was afraid that David would have gone with the troops that were sent there. It was a year of dazzling weather. Spring always had a sharpness and a clearness about it at Stunford.

We drove over to see Aunt May just outside Coventry. It was the first time I had driven any distance - about thirty miles. The countryside looked beautiful, bursting out into leaf.

Aunt May's cottage was very picturesque outside, but was rather cold and dark inside, with small windows. Downstairs the floors were stone flags, and the kitchen was little more than a scullery with a sink and a Valor Perfection oil stove to cook on, much like ours at Stunford. The owners had furnished the rooms in very unpleasant oak reproduction furniture. it was all the same shaded brown. There were nicknacks everywhere - horse brasses, little china cottages and figures. Aunt May had taken the pictures down and put them in a cupboard and collected the little mats that were on the tops of everything. She and my mother talked about old times. Even about Egypt. Harry, our very successful cousin, had gone into the Army.

May seemed very lost. She said she hardly knew a soul in the neighbourhood and each day was emptier than the last. Donald too, she said, was not enjoying his new life, never having had anything to do with manufacturing before.

"Perhaps this whole beastly business will come to an end soon and we'll all be able to go home," she sighed. We peered through a small upstairs window and looked across a field to a winding river. "That," May pointed out gloomily, "is the River Avon and we are in the Forest of Arden." "I do my shopping in Coventry. It's ancient and rather beautiful, I have to say, but all round about it are miles of ghastly little red brick houses, because of the factory workers."

"I've always wanted to see the Cathedral," my mother said. "In the Middle Ages, Coventry was the centre of ribbon making, but the Plague killed all the ribbon makers and the whole thing came to an end."

"You do come out with the most obscure bits of information, Marion," May remarked sourly. "Next time you come, we'll go and look at the Cathedral. By the way, I meant to tell you that Aunt Pamela has died." (Aunt Pamela was Granny Bell's sister. The family had tried to drag her south to the 80th birthday party that never happened.)

"I wonder who'll get all that satanic money? Not us, you may be sure."

CHAPTER 31

My Diary, 27th April:

I have started clearing the flower beds ready to plant vegetables. I have never done digging before; it has made me very stiff. I have asked Mrs. Attwood to get me some manure. Mr. Attwood, referred to as 'Our Dad' is coming to help with the clearing. He is a fine-looking man who owned a small farm at one time. He went bankrupt about ten years ago, and now they live in a three-roomed cottage.

Mrs. Havers came and told my mother that Aunt May had rung up and could we get in touch. Mrs. Havers said to my mother that far from the telephoning at the Vicarage being a trouble, it gave her a wonderful opportunity to walk over for a chat and, likewise, when we went over there it was lovely to see us.

She always brought the dog, Gillie, so Bristles had to be shut up. She and my mother were on Christian name terms - Marion and Muriel. Although the world was in turmoil, I foresaw clearly that our silly connection with the Vicarage held in it the seeds of disaster.

The crunch came one evening as it was getting dark, at the beginning of May. The Vicar drew up in his car. As I opened the door to him, I saw at once how cross he was.

"This telephoning business has got to stop," he almost shouted. "You really must tell your mother to get a telephone of her own installed. It is most inconvenient to turn out at this time. Muriel isn't well so, of course, I had to come. I haven't got the time to run about giving people telephone messages and answer phone calls at all times of the day and night to your relatives." He paused and took a breath, "Tonight's message," he said in a tense, tetchy way, "is that Violet has had a baby, born this morning at 4 o'clock." At that he turned, got in his car and drove off.

I found myself trembling. I rushed to tell my mother the news. Is it a boy or a girl?" she asked. He hadn't told me. The next morning I went to the Post Office and rang up the Warings to ask how Violet was and find out whether the baby was a boy or a girl. After that I had to get in touch with all the Aunts and tell them not to ring up the Vicarage any more. The whole village heard what I was saying. I hurried home to tell my mother that her grandchild was a boy.

The Post Office at Stunford was in a small stone cottage. The Post Mistress was Miss Annie Turner. It was she and her sister Winnie who had objected so strongly to the Ten Commandments behind the Altar in the church being covered up.

Miss Annie was very small, well under five foot. She served the customers through a square window cut in the wooden partition that divided her front room. She was so short that she had to stand on a wooden orange box to be able to look through the hole. On receiving a telegram she would often read it aloud for all to hear before putting it in its orange envelope. I suppose it was her way of checking it. If it was addressed to someone in the village, her sister Winnie was called upon to put on her elaborate hat and old coat and deliver it, but if it had to go to one of the outlying farms, their brother Gerald was summoned from the back room where he lurked, a perpetual presence. He would emerge stiffly, smelling pungently of rural man and tobacco and go and get his bicycle out of the shed and wobble off.

The only thing to be sold at the Post Office beside stamps were seeds. On the wall by the door hung a rack holding the packets. Coloured pictures of successful flowers and huge shining vegetables lit up the damp gloom. The telephone was behind the wooden partition, on the counter: the vital nerve centre of the village.

We went at once to London to visit Violet and see the baby.

It was a long bus ride to where the Warings lived and a long walk to their house. The numbers were alternate and we found it with difficulty. Every house was like every other house, except for unbearable details, but it was the beginning of May and the little gardens were full of flowering trees and spring flowers.

Mrs. Waring opened the door. She looked worse at home than when we'd seen her before. The whole house smelt of dinner and the expression on her face was so exasperatingly kind.

"Come in," she said, "come in. You've come to see the little gift, I expect." We went upstairs. Violet was lying in bed in the front bedroom. I thought she looked very unwell and tired. Beside her in the cot was the baby. We looked closely at him. You are expected to look closely at new babies. "I won't disturb him, if you don't mind," Violet said, "if I do, he'll cry."

"Violet doesn't feel very confident yet," Mrs. Waring told us. "I keep reminding her how lucky she is to have mother at hand. When I had Stephen, I had no one to turn to. I just had to get on with it and learn as I went along."

"What are you going to call him?" my mother asked.

Violet replied faintly, "I wanted him to be called Gareth, but David thinks John is nicer. David was here yesterday, but he's had to go back this morning. He gave me those lovely flowers." She pointed to some bought roses stuck in a glass jug on the dressing table.

The room where Violet lay faced north. In spite of the warm sunny weather, it felt chilly and the light was harsh and searching. It was sparsely furnished but untidy. There were things left about everywhere. This seemed to worry Mrs. Waring, because she kept bobbing about putting things away and hanging up clothes. In a way it helped because no one could think of anything to say. Violet shut her eyes and Mrs. Waring brought us cups of tea and white bread and butter. My mother made some mention of the news. Mrs. Waring dismissed the remark by saying, "I try to remind myself all the time that it is only the works of Satan." I could see that my mother was going to speak, but she said nothing, to my relief.

A clock at the end of their road struck six.

After having another look at the baby, there was a round of ritual kissing, which was obviously expected.

Just as we were leaving, a friend of Violet's arrived to see her, a serious, nice-looking girl. I found out afterwards that she was from their church.

The ride home was interminable: people getting on and getting off, stopping and starting and stopping and starting. When it was time for us to get off ourselves, I felt I would rather not make the effort, just stay on the bus forever.

CHAPTER 32

The day on which we went to see Violet and the baby, was the day the Germans attacked. We heard it on the evening news. They were smashing their way through Holland and Belgium.

Day after day the news got worse, and then came the evacuation of our troops from Dunkirk. It was the long period of summer weather that made it possible - the sun shone from a cloudless sky onto the calm Channel.

My mother said, "We've left Bristles for far too long, we must go back to Stunford and see how he is getting on."

A woman on the train exclaimed, "Do you know what - we've lost this bloody war, that's what!"

My mother replied, "You mustn't say things like that - it's treason!"

"Tell that to the Germans," the woman retorted. "I don't know where my boy is, do I? He's out there somewhere," and she started to cry.

Those were feverish days. No one knew what was going to happen. The almost certain threat of invasion was in everyone's mind. At Stunford the headmaster from the village school came to our door. He told us that it was thought likely that paratroops would be dropped on this high ground and from here sweep down on to the industrial cities of the Midlands.

"I have been sent to tell everyone to dig deep pits in their gardens so that if there is an airborne landing, all food can be quickly hidden, and if a situation should arise where they do take food, it is your duty to lace it with any poisons or laxatives in your possession."

It was hard to take it seriously. Such imminent danger was too hard to realise. I wondered if we would ever see Ian, David and the new baby again. It was all so terrifying.

Yesterday we drove over to see Aunt May. We thought it might be the last time because of the petrol. All the signposts had been taken down. I went the wrong way at the crossroads, just after Shipston. I asked a woman pushing a pram the way to

Leamington and we got on the right road again. We were twice stopped by the police: they asked us who we were. One policeman asked me if we had been stopped before. He squeezed my hand and winked at me. We missed the turning and found ourselves driving through Warwick.

In Warwick there was an extraordinary sight. On the pavements, all through the town, there were exhausted soldiers; some lying, some sitting, many of them asleep. I suppose they had just come back from Dunkirk and were waiting for somewhere to go. They didn't seem to have any equipment, only gas-masks in cardboard boxes hanging round their necks with string - like the ones we had. (The Germans were advancing right into the middle of France.)

We had hoped to go and see Coventry Cathedral, but didn't because of the petrol.

When we got to Aunt May's, she and my mother were obviously pleased to see each other and had a good talk. They swopped all the family news, but their conversation soon deteriorated into what the Bells called 'feather picking'. Aunt May started it - they had been discussing the progress of the war and how awful it all was, when Aunt May said, "Quite apart from anything else, I can't bear to think of Harry wasting his time, when he should be getting on with his academic career." My mother was clearly irritated.

"It's the same for all of them, and I expect it will do him no end of good to get away from his books for a while. Straighten him up a bit and give him a wider view of life, and help his eyesight."

This silenced May for a moment, but not for long.

"It's all very well for you to talk, none of your children are brilliant like Harry." She paused. "There's a woman down the road, I can't remember her name, she told me she'd been to a chemist in Coventry and asked him for some poison to give her daughters in case the Germans came. The chemist shushed her, and told her she'd find herself shut up if she went round saying things like that." May added, under her breath, "If I were you, I'd be afraid for Hannah."

At that point I left them to it and took myself off into the garden, where I found a little gate that opened onto a field and a way down to the river. I wandered over and sat on the bank and watched the water flow past. There was a slight breeze; the sun was shining through the leaves of the great trees, and the birds were flitting amongst the branches. On the opposite bank, two ponies were grazing, swishing their tails. I thought of the river at Marchfold, and wished and wished that everything were different.

When I got back to the cottage, they were still arguing, bickering about whose fault it was that Marchfold hadn't been sold in time.

"I think we'd better go," my mother said, getting up. We departed in silence.

* * * * *

I have been reading recently the speech that Churchill made to Parliament on 8th June 1940. Even I, who heard it broadcast at the time, had largely forgotten it. (The speech over the air was, in fact, delivered by an actor-impersonator. Churchill was too busy to do it himself. No one could have guessed.) It was the famous, 'We shall fight on the beaches,' speech:

'We shall fight on the landing grounds, we shall fight in the fields and on the streets, we shall fight in the hills, we shall never surrender. Even if - which I do not for a moment believe - if this land or a large part of it were subjugated and starving, then our Empire beyond the seas, armed and guarded by the British Fleet, would carry on the struggle until in God's good time the New World with all its power and might, steps forth to the rescue and the liberation of the Old.' He continued by saying, 'Now Britain faces the imminent threat of invasion, but Napoleon failed and so too will Hitler.'

Chapter 33

My mother and I became rather unwell.

Dr. Brand, the village doctor, lived just round the corner from us. I asked Mrs. Attwood if she would kindly go and ask him to call. He came next day just before lunch. He walked straight into my mother's bedroom and looked at her lying in bed. "What do you think is wrong with you?" he asked. He didn't examine her, but just stood beside her. "I expect you've got what a lot of people have got at the moment. In a couple of days it will pass. I won't give you any medicine, there wouldn't be any point." Then he turned and looked at me. "And I expect you've got it too. My wife and I had it last week."

I have seldom seen anyone so bored and uninterested. He was a sandy little man with wire-rimmed spectacles.

It was then he noticed Bristles lying curled up on my mother's feet. Immediately his attitude changed. He became infused with enthusiasm and interest, and became our friend.

"What a lovely cat. My wife and I are great cat lovers. We have six," he said, stroking him. "What's happened to his ear?" (He had been fighting with the criminal cat from the knitting party house.) "I think you ought to bathe that ear with warm water, with a little salt in it, perhaps. I'll give you the address of the vet that we use. He's excellent - Mr. Bredon, such a nice man."

He lingered over Bristles and then pulled up a chair and sat down and started to talk.

"My wife and I are great walkers. We enjoy walking the bridle ways and footpaths all round the country. We were near Bicester once and we found a cat beside the railway line. She was terribly thin and blind in one eye. We picked her up and brought her home ... We christened her Jemima. She's really quite old now. Of course, we didn't know how old she was when we found her." Then he went on to tell us how they had acquired every cat. Neither my mother nor I felt at all well and we were longing for him to go, but he stayed and stayed.

He got up to go. "You'll soon be better," he assured us, and looking at me said, "What do you do with yourself all day? There are no young people here, that's the trouble. My daughters find it very boring during the school holidays, I'm afraid."

My mother mentioned the news.

"We never listen to the wireless," he answered. "You see, my wife and I don't believe in war!"

While we were still ill Mrs. Havers called with the awful dog. My mother remembered to call her Murial.

"I've come to say how sorry I am that Charles was so impatient about the telephone. You mustn't take any notice, and I have to congratulate you on becoming a grandmother. I'm one myself now. My daughter had her baby two days ago - it's a little girl. She's going to be called Theresa. They're coming down to stay with us, so we shall see her then. I was sorry to hear that you weren't well, but I thought I'd stay away till you were a little better. I didn't want to catch whatever it was. I've only just got better from the last thing I had."

She was dressed in an ill-fitting flowery cotton dress and sandals. She too stayed interminably.

Amazingly, my mother's friendship with Mrs. Havers survived the telephone episode.

Italy joined in the war. The French had capitulated and the Germans were in Paris and they had occupied the Channel Islands.

Ian came home on leave because he was going abroad. We didn't know then that he was going to Canada to train as a bomber pilot. The beautiful summer weather continued, but he was very restless and preoccupied. My mother wouldn't leave him alone. She kept asking him if anything was wrong. He found it very irksome.

"Do you think Ian's alright?" she asked me a hundred times. "I'm sure something's the matter. Don't you think he's got something on his mind?"

Ian enquired about Dr. Brand and went to see him. I wondered why. He told me later when we went for a walk while Mother had a rest.

We sat down on some rough grass on the edge of a cornfield,

and listened to the larks as they climbed singing into the cloudless sky above the corn.

Ian lay back and closed his eyes.

I fiddled with my shoe lace.

"I've got to say something to you, Ian," I mumbled. "I know I promised you that I wouldn't leave Mother while you were both away. Things have changed so much since then. As soon as I'm old enough, I want to join one of the forces. I realise that someone will have to be found to be in the house with Mother."

Ian sat up. "Hannah, you've just got to stay. It's your duty. With me away and David gone, you have no choice."

"But the war may go on for years, perhaps all our lives," I pleaded.

"You know I went to see Dr. Brand. If girls have to register for war work or are called up, he says he'll see you get exempted for compassionate reasons."

When Ian left, Mother took to her bed for two days. She didn't eat anything either. I was worried. When she got up, we went to London. We found that all the railings round the Square Garden and our garden had been sawn off and taken away to be melted down to make guns. There was litter on the spacious lawns and rude writing on the summer-house walls.

CHAPTER 34

While the Battle of Britain was going on in the air, I said, "How I wish we were at Marchfold; then at least we would feel we were in the middle of things."

Mr. Churchill told the Commons that he expected the Germans to invade within the week.

We had a letter from David. He wrote that four of his friends from Westminster had been lost at sea. All of them had joined the Merchant Navy - all of them had supported the 'this House will not fight for King and Country' motion in the school debating society. I remembered them at the summer Sunday teas in London. I found it hard to realise that they were at the bottom of the Atlantic. It seemed an impossibility.

The days were interminable, punctuated only by meals and the news. Most of the vegetables I had planted were a failure. The birds ate the peas and the carrots were eaten by mice or slugs. I spent hours picking the caterpillars off the cabbages and broccoli.

Every time we went to London, I brought back a suitcase full of books from our bookshelves. I had suddenly started to read. I read everything I could lay my hands on. I had also begun to bemoan the fact that I had never bothered to learn anything at school and that I would probably regret it for the rest of my life. These depressing thoughts mingled with the emptiness of the days and the terrible fears about what was likely to happen.

The sight of the Home Guard drilling in the village did not evoke confidence. The greatcoats they wore were all the same size, so that the small men had coats to the ground, while the tall ones' knees were visible. They carried the pikes with which they had been issued. No other weapons were available. Mrs. Attwood said, covering her mouth, "They're enough to make a cat laugh." The Misses Turner's brother was one of the small ones: his boots were almost covered and his hands completely hidden by the sleeves.

We heard from Violet that her brother had joined the Fire Service. She wrote nice little letters to my mother now and again, giving her scraps of news about David and the baby.

Then the Blitz started. It began with a daylight raid on the City. Warehouses in the docks were set on fire. Blazing rum ran in the gutters and paint and sugar floated down the Thames. Violet's brother told us afterwards that many of his fellow firemen scooped up the rum and drank it, and became utterly incapable. He didn't join in because he was a teetotaller, but he said he was so frightened that he wished he was as drunk as they were.

My Diary, 4th September:

Violet arrived today with the baby. It was late afternoon when the taxi drew up. It was piled with masses of luggage. A cot, the pram, suitcases and a lot of hats. What she wants with hats, I can't think. We have put her in the room that was full of Ian's things, because it is the biggest. We moved them to my room and piled them up. It doesn't leave me with much space, but what does it matter?

The taxi man was very kind and helped me to get the cot upstairs and put together.

Violet looked very pale, I thought. "I promised David I would leave if the bombing started," she said. She is lucky to be so pretty. She was worn out and went to lie down after a cup of tea. She asked me to call her in an hour's time and handed me the baby.

That was my first real encounter with Johnie - Johnie, whom I grew to love so much over the stormy years that followed. When Violet handed him to me that evening, I was horrified and I was afraid. I was afraid of killing him somehow without knowing it. I couldn't think what to do, so I carried him out into the garden and sat down on the little stone seat under the apple tree. The branches were loaded with apples and weighed down all round us, as though we were in a tent. The evening light filtered through the leaves and onto the windfalls that lay on the ground, buzzing with wasps and flies. Johnie made small alive noises from all the shawls that Violet had wrapped him in.

142

Mrs. Attwood had told me it was time for the apples to be picked.

After some time, my mother came looking for us. "What are you doing out there?" she called. "Don't let the baby get cold."

When Violet got up from her little rest, she was rather distraught because of the journey alone with the baby and with the upset of the air raids. She was breastfeeding Johnie and the next thing that happened was that her milk dried up. Their first night at Chapel House was terrible - Violet wept and Johnie cried. I went to Banbury first thing next morning to buy dried babymilk and bottles. Johnie refused, screaming, to even try it. He arched his back and went purple in the face. After tasting it at last, he spat it out. My mother went into her bedroom and shut her door against the din - "I never was very good with babies," she said.

At Mrs. Attwood's suggestion, I went round to Dr. Brand's house. His wife opened the door. She had nice-coloured very homespun clothes on and her hair was looped up in a Pre-Raphaelite sort of way. I told her about our desperate plight. She wasn't very helpful. "You're rather young, aren't you, to take all this on," she said, looking at me rather disparagingly.

She then went on to say, "I'll get the District Nurse to call on you as soon as she can. I don't expect it'll be before tomorrow now. She's run off her feet anyway."

We had another hideous night. Violet was on the brink of madness when Nurse Wickins arrived. She immediately dominated the situation - she took control like someone who can make wild horses docile without appearing to do anything specific. One look from her, and Johnie knew he'd met his match. Violet became calmer and more hopeful. It was a miracle. The whole scene was changed. Over a period of a few days Violet's milk came back. Nurse Wickins came every day for about a week. I was so thankful.

My Diary, 20th September:
Nurse Wickins came again this morning - she has a round red face and the biggest bottom I have ever seen and the tightest nurse's belt. Her legs look like skittles in her black stockings.

Her presence though is very reassuring. She thanked me when I took her a cup of tea, which was nice, and she asked me my name and how old I was. My mother had a chat with her. They talked about the air raids and the children being re-evacuated to the country again. She said she wasn't surprised that Violet's milk had dried up.

Mrs. Attwood never had much time for Violet. She was critical of her even from the first moment of arrival. Violet was a great sitter and hardly ever lent a hand. My mother was a sitter too, but that came on her after my father's death. They hardly ever sat in the same room though, except at meal times. Mrs. Attwood said about Violet, "I don't know what the world is coming to, when a girl doesn't know how to look after her own baby."

We had just got over the screaming Johnie crisis, when the Billeting Officer (not Miss Bates this time, but somebody else) came to the house. She brought a little girl with her. In spite of my mother's protests, she left her with us.

The poor child was very small and thin for her age. We discovered that she was 10 years old. Round her neck was a label with her name on - Maria Gabrielli, and her address.

She had her gas-mask and a small cardboard suitcase, broken at the corners.

When she arrived she was trembling.

We heaped up Ian's things in my bedroom and made room to put up a camp bed for her so that she wouldn't be alone.

How dreadful it must have been for the little girl to be dumped with strangers, away from everybody and everything she had ever known. Removed from the clamour of her family and city life, the silent countryside must have added to the shock of the Blitz.

For the first few weeks she hardly ate or spoke, except to whisper now and again, "I want me Nan."

We found out that her mother had died and that she had been brought up by her grandmother who had kept house for her father. There were two elder brothers, both of them recently called up.

My mother tried very hard to encourage her and make her

feel better by telling her stories and reading to her, but the thing that helped her most was Bristles. She never left off lugging him about, and hugging him so hard, that she squeezed all the air out of him. He was endlessly patient, and only scratched her once, which was by accident.

When the autumn term at the village school started, it was arranged for her to go there and she gradually settled down.

She hardly ever spoke of home, but once told us that her grandfather "had done something terrible wrong, and I gone with my Nan to see Father Patrick, and he said, 'Don't fret yourselves, it's the drink'."

Maria very much admired Violet and tried to copy the way she spoke, which was rather over careful, and after a while she began to speak precisely herself. She called me 'Han' and my mother 'Missis', but Violet she always called 'Violet'.

Bristles always slept on my mother's bed. Maria made a habit of coming down in her nightdress very early in the morning and opening my mother's bedroom door, saying in a loud whisper, "Is Bristles available?" My mother found this very irritating and blamed Violet for talking in such a silly way.

CHAPTER 35

My Diary, 23rd Oct:
Violet isn't well. Nurse Wickins got Dr. Brand to come and see her. He says that she must stay in bed for a few days. He gave her some medicine, which gave her a bad pain, so I have to look after Johnie. I took him out with me in his pram, while I was picking the apples. I put the apples into a great heap in the wooden shed beside the garage. In about two weeks each apple has to be wrapped in newspaper. In this way, I am told they will keep and can be used all through the winter.

David suddenly turned up in a taxi. He was upset to find Violet so unwell. She got up because he had come, but she had to go back to bed. She cried all evening.

My mother was delighted to see David, but of course he spent all his time in Violet's bedroom, talking to her and he had his meals with her as well.

24th Oct:
Dr. Brand came again. He told Violet if she wasn't better soon she would have to into hospital. Today we had two letters from Ian telling us about Canada and how much he is loving it. David went back. Violet was very upset and I could see that David was upset too.

25th Oct:
Violet is much better and able to get up. Whatever seemed to be wrong with her has cleared up.

Violet asked my mother if her parents could come down to stay for a few days: "they are exhausted by being up all night and not sleeping because of the raids and need some undisturbed nights."

Two days later the Warings turned up. They brought a great deal of luggage with them. It had to be stacked in the hall. Dr. Brand had told Violet not to lift anything, so she couldn't help with the stacking. My mother whispered to me anxiously behind the door, "it looks as though they've come for a long time." They moved into the only empty bedroom, upstairs next to mine.

When they first arrived they were so grateful to be given quiet nights that nothing was too much trouble for them to do in the house. No effort too great to remain pleasant in the face of difficulties. But gradually this wore off. They became sullen and discontented. If they weren't silent, they were comparing the delights of living in London to the dreariness of the countryside. I suppose it must have been the reaction to the fear and stress that they had been through. Nevertheless, it was hard to bear.

The atmosphere in the house was far from happy. For one thing, Mrs. Waring didn't like listening to the wireless and objected to having it on for the news. Every time my mother turned it on to hear the latest bulletin, Mrs. Waring would get up and walk out. On one occasion she declared, "We all know that the Devil is walking through the world, but that doesn't mean to say we have to listen to him all the time."

Mr. Waring didn't like cats, and Bristles constantly tormented him, just as he had done when they visited us in London.

Two weeks passed. My mother eyed the luggage in the hall with increasing irritation. Mrs. Waring was constantly wanting something out of the suitcases - usually what she wanted was in the trunk at the bottom of the pile.

"It isn't good for you, Hannah, to lift those great weights," my mother said, as I was struggling to find a dark pink tweed skirt that had been requested.

Things got increasingly difficult and then came to a head when Mrs. Waring asked my mother if she could have a word with her in private, and followed her into the bedroom. She shut the door behind her.

"I've been wondering if the little evacuee girl has been christened. It's worried me no end. Do you suppose she could be a pagan?"

My mother was very taken aback and replied, "I would hardly think so. From what I understand her family are Roman Catholics."

Mrs. Waring carried on, "The other thing I wanted to speak about is the damp in this house. Did you know that there is a patch of damp in the corner of Violet's room? My clothes feel damp when I come to put them on in the morning. It could be dangerous for the baby and not good for Violet."

"What do you expect me to do about it?" my mother asked, her voice rising. "Do you not realise that the world is falling apart, and you come and whine to me about a patch of damp."

Mrs. Waring started to cry. "You could have more heating."

At this my mother exploded. "What about the fuel, I don't suppose you've thought of that?"

"You could burn wood."

"You go and cut a tree down and saw it up and carry it in and light it, you stupid woman!" my mother shouted. "To start with, we haven't even got a tree, except the apple tree. Perhaps you'd like to chop that down or get your husband to do it."

This argument could be heard all over the house. Presently Mr. Waring came and led his wife away, and Violet comforted her in the kitchen.

Mrs. Attwood was in the scullery at the time, listening. "It was as good as a picture show," she said afterwards. "I couldn't help but laugh."

The next day the Warings went back to London. Nearly all their things were left behind. My mother said she thought it was unwise to say anything because it might delay their departure.

After Violet's parents had gone, there was rather an atmosphere between us and her. I said in my diary, Violet is a bit frosty.

The night of the 14th, there was a great pulsation of aeroplanes going overhead. We knew they must be German bombers. They flew over all night and hadn't gone until daylight came. Maria got into my bed. She was trembling. In the morning we heard what had happened - Coventry had been razed to the ground and it was now a heap of smouldering rubble. We thought of Aunt May. I went to telephone, but no lines were working. We decided we must go over and see if she was alright.

We had been allocated an allowance of 5 gallons of petrol a month, because of living so far out in the country. We considered ourselves lucky to have got any at all. There was some petrol in the tank of the car and we still had three coupons in hand.

Violet was rather plaintive about being left alone with Johnie and Maria, but we took no notice and set off.

The roads were deserted. In the whole day we only met two cars and an army convoy of trucks. We passed a crashed German bomber lying in a field like a broken bird. There were several people standing beside it, staring, and a policeman, who must have been making them keep their distance. His bicycle was propped up against the hedge.

We left the car and went over to have a look ourselves. When we got close, I asked the policeman what had happened to the crew. "Bailed out," he said, "but they didn't get far."

When we arrived at Aunt May's village, nothing looked changed but the sky was dark and the air thick with smoke. Inside her house there were mattresses and camp beds all over the floors. Some people were asleep, others sat staring into space.

Aunt May flung her arms round my mother. "Come and look," she said. We climbed up the bank at the back of the house and from there we saw the smouldering rubble that had been the city of Coventry. The Cathedral spire was still standing amongst the ruins, just visible through the smoke. May said, "They're still trying to dig people out. We spent last night putting incendiaries out. There were some caught in the apple trees. We were afraid that if we left them alight they might drop other bombs."

We helped May cut bread and make hot drinks and washed up mugs. While we were busy, a woman came in. She was very grimy and shocked-looking. She was carrying a small terrier-type dog. It was trembling, just like Maria. "One of the heavy rescue men dug this dog out and handed it to me. What am I going to do with it? It's not mine," she said. "It'll have to be put down, I can't keep it."

"Give it to me," I said, "I'll have it." I thought Mother was going to stop me, but she didn't.

It was autumn, a sad time of the year anyway, and the leaves were beginning to turn; mist was rising from the river, mingling with the smell of burning and dust. We wanted to get home before evening because of the blackout-paper that covered our head lamps and made it very difficult to see in the dark. Before we left, someone sitting on a mattress was given bad news.

"I don't know what Bristles will say about this dog," my mother remarked as we got into the car. "What are we going to give it to eat, dogs don't have meat coupons!"

"He's not a big dog, except that he is a she."

She sat on Mother's lap, still shivering like Maria.

When we got home, we heard the sirens going in Banbury.

With the blackout curtains drawn tightly, and the fire flickering, we sat round the table in a warm circle of light eating scrambled eggs and bread. Suddenly I felt a completely selfish feeling. I thought how lucky we were to be safe and warm and have something to eat. I felt very guilty because of all the dead and perhaps still alive people under the rubble in Coventry.

"I'm so thankful that Ian is out of it in Canada," my mother said, "and I'm glad your father is out of it too."

Her words wrenched me.

Maria looked up from her plate and asked Violet if she had ever had worms. Violet was taken aback.

"Not that I know of - worms are not a thing we really mention at the table."

I could see that my mother was annoyed with Violet.

"When I lived in foreign parts, far away, I had worms," she said, "huge ones as big as knitting needles."

"What a conversation," Violet exclaimed, "and while we're eating at the table."

Maria realised she had said something wrong, and was confused and upset.

My mother helped her by saying, "Go and see where Bristles is." She got down from the table and came back with him. He struggled free and got up on my mother's lap. Maria lent over my mother's knee and buried her face in his fur.

Johnie was asleep in his pram beside us. He started to cry so Violet picked him up and gave him to me, while she got his milk.

Suddenly I felt trapped and frustrated. I wished I were anywhere but in that room, at that time, sitting at that table. The soft glow of light which had been so comforting before had become suffocating and restrictive. There didn't seem to be any way out, or a future beyond the hopeless situation I found myself in. I looked at my mother and felt ashamed because I loved her.

About this time, during the night, the Germans were dropping whistling bombs here and there, wherever they saw any glimpse of life or activity. The screaming noise they made when coming down was intended to frighten and demoralise.

While Violet was feeding Johnie, two whistling bombs came down a little way off. Maria covered her face with her hands tightly, and stayed like that until she went to bed.

As soon as Violet had regained her strength, she started going to church. She went regularly to the early service. The vicar soon called on us again to make her acquaintance, and our connection and friendship with the vicar and his wife took a turn for the better, and even flourished.

My Diary:

With our combined meat coupons, I am able to buy a leg of lamb once a month. I make it last for a long time - days and days. We have it cold, minced, hashed, cold again. Several times I started to cook our meal and discovered that there wasn't as much meat left on the bone as I had thought. Then I found that Violet was in the habit of nipping into the larder now and then and cutting herself a slice or two. I told my mother because I felt that it was impossible to speak to Violet about it. But eventually I had to. I said, "If you help yourself to meat, there won't be enough to last for other people. If you feel hungry, there's always bread." She replied, "I've been meaning to say for some time that I'd like to have my butter and margarine separate, so that I can eat it when I want to without having to explain. After all, I'm still feeding Johnie. Admittedly not much, but it makes me ravenous."

Feeding the dog was much more difficult than I had thought. Of course, on the spur of the moment I had been carried away and dismissed all difficulties, but in reality it was a constant battle. We gave her scraps and bread and milk, and occasionally a rabbit shot by Mr. Attwood. He showed me how to paunch and skin them - an unenviable, disgusting job. The thought of eating rabbit all these years later is still sick-making.

The little dog was named Rubble, which later became Rabby. Her great use was to chase the criminal cat from The Croft out of the garden, but she had a pale personality and was always aloof and timid, and dominated by Bristles - possibly because of what had happened to her.

CHAPTER 36

My Diary:

David has come home on embarkation leave. We vaguely think he is going to the Far East. My mother said, "That's a good thing - it will mean that he will probably be away from all the fighting and I shan't have to worry."

My mother and I were listening to the 6 o'clock news when there was an explosion. The news reader paused for a second or two and then went on with the news. We now know that a bomb had passed through the studio and exploded on a floor below, killing seven people.

David and Violet decided to go away alone together for a few days. Violet asked me to look after Johnie, but then David wanted to take him.

They had to have the car, and went to a pub only ten miles away. It was difficult to find anywhere to stay, because bombed-out people from Coventry had taken all the rooms to be had for miles around.

My mother was upset that David wanted to go off. "Why doesn't he want to stay here with us?" she complained miserably.

A little more than a week later they came back. The next day David left. We went to Banbury Station. David drove and Violet sat beside him in the front. I had to go with them because of driving home. I sat in the back. My mother stayed at home. When we got to the station Violet said to me, "Do you mind staying in the car, while I see David off? I need to be alone with him."

After David's departure, Violet was unbearably unhappy and, although she became used to him being away, she remained more or less like that all the time. I think Johnie suffered from the sadness.

So we carried on from day to day, managing ourselves and our problems as best we could. Our difficulties were comparatively unimportant, except emotionally.

My Diary:

It's my birthday - I am eighteen.

My mother said, "Hannah, I would give you anything in the world, if I could." Violet said, "I'm sorry I haven't got you a present or even a card, being so far away from the shops makes everything so difficult. The next time I go to Banbury I'll get you something."

It is much colder - I suppose it is winter. I have read all the books that we brought from London. We shall have to go and get some more. I wrapped up all the apples in squares of newspaper. It may stop them from getting frosted and keep them from going bad.

At 18 all my contemporaries were joining the forces or doing vital work of some sort or another. I was reading and hearing all the time about inspiring deeds of self-sacrifice and incredible courage. I longed passionately to join in the battle for the freedom of the world. Instead, I was destined to heat kettles of hot water so that my mother could wash in the morning, and heat other kettles for Violet and Johnie, and more kettles for Maria and me. Once a month I lighted the huge old coke boiler - that was if we had any coke. Mrs. Attwood took all our general washing home, where she had an old-fashioned wood-fired copper just like the one Ivy and Ellen had in their cottage.

CHAPTER 37

I was drawing the blackout curtains, when I heard a knock at the door. It was Miss Turner from the Post Office, in her garden party hat. Terrible things raced through my mind, but I quickly realised that both the boys were accounted for. The telegram was for Violet, from her brother. It read: "Bombed out. Bringing Father tomorrow."

Violet read it to my mother, who was far from pleased and didn't disguise the fact in spite of the extreme circumstances. Violet was puzzled. "Mother must be going to Auntie Jean," she said. "I expect she'll be better off there anyway."

Violet's father and brother Stephen turned up in a taxi. Mr. Waring's face was very bruised and cut. One of his hands was very swollen. Both of them were grey with fatigue and shock. Neither of them had shaved and they were still covered with dust. Violet's mother had been killed in the blast and everything they possessed was lost. Mr. Waring hadn't even got a toothbrush.

Violet and I looked through the boxes that they had left with us. Most of the things were Mrs. Waring's, but we found some jerseys, a cricket blazer and a pair of socks of his.

Violet's brother Stephen told us what had happened. At the time of the raid, the Warings were sleeping in the dining-room under the table for safety. The house came down on top of them. When Mr. Waring came to in hospital after being dug out, he asked where his wife was. Nobody knew. He got up from his hospital bed and started looking for her. Later he was joined by Stephen and together they traipsed from one hospital to another, and from morgue to morgue. Towards evening, they found her.

Violet was devastated when she heard that her mother had been killed, but she pulled herself together. She was very good to her father.

The Vicar heard of the tragedy and he came round, bringing a jacket and a pair of trousers. Unfortunately, he was a much bigger and taller man than Mr. Waring, and had what Mrs. Attwood called a 'high stomach'. He stayed a long time trying to console Violet and talked at length to Mr. Waring. I could see that they didn't really want to be talked to.

Stephen went back to London the next day to make the necessary arrangements. He said he had made up his mind to leave the fire service and join the Army. His father said, "What would your mother say?"

Maria was very upset by all this and put her hands over her face again. I couldn't find her, but I later discovered her sitting on the floor of the bathroom. The following morning she sought out Bristles and I heard her say to him, "It's not so bad today, Bristles," so I knew she was better.

As we had used up all the month's petrol, I had to take the village bus to Banbury. It went once a week on Thursdays, picking up people from the villages on the way. I simply had to get poor Mr. Waring a few necessities of life, like shaving things and pants.

I had never been on the bus before. When I boarded it, many meaningful glances were exchanged and there were nudges all round. Those who have not experienced village life will hardly realise what an intimidating experience it was, but I weathered it somehow and did the shopping in time to catch the bus back. The return journey, if anything, was worse because the passengers were curious about what was in my parcels. One fat woman actually spoke to me. "Sent to run the family errands, eh?" she said. The chattering ceased for a minute, a pause in breath, while everybody waited for me to reply.

Nearly all the people on the bus were middle-aged women. There were only one or two elderly men, sitting at the back, smoking their pipes, taking no part in the gossip or the inane shrieks that accompanied it.

My Diary:
Violet has had some letters from David. My mother hasn't had one yet. I doubt if she will, but she did have one from Ian. He has got his wings, but is being made to stay on in Canada to train other pilots. This doesn't please him at all, because he can't wait to come home and start flying on operations - he has

met the Havers' son, Andrew, out there. He says that he is the nicest person.

Miss Bates came and brought a whole lot of clothes that had belonged to a dead brother. They were for Mr. Waring. They weren't a bad fit, but the poor man looked very forlorn when trying them on. There were some shoes, but they were hopeless, being far too big.

Violet said, "My father is not able to easily come downstairs to the bathroom in the night, do you think he could have a chamber pot?" We didn't have one, but when Nurse Wickins next visited Violet, we asked her if she had such a thing. "Bedpans, yes, but pots, no," adding, "why don't you give the poor gentleman a pudding basin?"

My mother was very put out when he regularly emptied the contents of this pudding basin out of his upstairs window onto the flowerbed below, which was just outside her window. When a smell developed, she said, "Mr. Waring, I would be grateful if you would ask your daughter to carry your slops down for you and get rid of them in the bathroom. You're swamping the plants in the flowerbed and it's started to smell."

Another kettle was added to the hot water ritual now that Mr. Waring was living with us.

My mother groaned in despair, "I suppose he's going to be with us forever." It certainly looked like it. The wretched man spent most of the time in his bedroom, only coming down from time to time to get warm in the kitchen.

Violet had great trouble over what to call my mother. She called her, 'Mother' awkwardly, when she remembered; but she normally said, 'Mrs. Brocus'. Sometimes it was 'Mrs. Brocus - I mean - Mother'.

I decorated the house with holly and ivy on Christmas Eve. There was no midnight service for Violet. We had been invited to the Vicarage for Christmas Day for their evening meal. Our contribution to the festivities was a plum pudding (which we had had for some time) and some brandy margarine. The margarine had been saved up for several weeks beforehand. My mother persuaded Mr. Waring to come, but he didn't really want to.

When it was time to go, we set out walking in the dark, pushing Johnie in his pram. I remember wishing that Mr. Waring would get a move on. Maria dragged her feet.

When we arrived at the house, we found Mrs. Havers distraught with the preparations. Getting the meal ready and the war seemed to be inextricably tangled in her mind. My mother talked to her about Ian. She had had a letter from her son Andrew. "He has just finished his training," - she was vaguely tearful.

When we were seated round the table, I looked across at Mr. Waring and thought how ill he looked. Not only did he look ill, he was juddering. He picked up his glass to drink some of Mrs. Havers' home-made wine and his hand shook so violently that some was spilt on his table-mat. My mother put her hand out to steady and comfort him.

"I'm afraid we haven't got turkey," Mrs. Havers announced. "We've got three guinea-fowl instead. I bought them from Mr. Turnbull on the bottom road. I expect you've seen them when you've walked past, all roosting in the larch tree!"

Mr. Havers made no great effort at conversation. "I'm rather tired, I'm afraid," he said. "What with all the services and rushing off to Marlington as well, I'm exhausted."

We had taken very uninteresting presents to exchange amongst ourselves, like handkerchiefs and pieces of soap. My mother gave Mrs. Havers a purple chiffon scarf that had been given to her several years before and never worn, and Mrs. Havers gave her a scarf but - judging from the look of it - one that she had worn.

To Maria's excitement, we had crackers. In them were trinkets and riddles. Maria got a little gold necklace, which broke before the evening was over. I remember now one of the riddles: 'What sort of a man is like a cup and saucer?' and the answer read out after a pause for people to guess, was 'A Chinaman'. The fat dog lay under the table, giving off his hot smell. Mrs. Havers continually slipped him bits.

CHAPTER 38

Before the end of 1940 there was a firebomb raid on the City of London. It was devastating. It prompted my mother to decide to put all the furniture from No. 12 into store and this was arranged. We travelled to London to see the stuff packed and the removal vans leave. The house looked terribly empty. I took as many books away as I could carry. There was an air raid warning while we were there, and the train home from Paddington was delayed two hours. When we got back to Stunford, we were tired, hungry and dirty. I never thought I'd be grateful to get back to Chapel House.

Violet hadn't got any supper ready for our return. She said, "I didn't know what you'd want; Father wasn't hungry and Maria has been eating bread."

We had a letter from Vanessa. She had been down to Sussex.

'I'm writing to tell you that Marchfold has been commandeered. Not, as I imagined, for an Officers' Mess, but to store furniture from bombed-out London houses. When I saw it, I couldn't believe my eyes - the windows were all boarded up. It looked as though it had been blinded. The flowerbeds have all but disappeared.

By the way, Ellen has died. I went to see Ivy. She seems to have got very mixed up about which war this is. I wouldn't be surprised if she thought it was the Boer War. Rather strange really, when the Battle of Britain took place in the sky above her head.'

A list of those men on active service was read out at nearly all of the church services, David and Ian Brocus amongst them. The list grew in length as time went by and more and more people were called up. There were no evening services in winter, only in the summer when it was light. It would have been impossible to black out such big, long windows.

Very occasionally, I went with Violet. Sometimes we were the only congregation. I used to sit there hoping that something would happen to me - it never did. I wondered if anything ever happened to Violet. Once at evensong in September, with the evening gathering round us and sounds of the countryside wafting through the wide open doors, I felt it was beautiful and comforting. The two candles on the altar flickered, and if I squeezed my eyes together, the light round them became a halo of colours. Mr. Havers was getting through the service as quickly as he could. He said the prayers so fast that the words ran one into another. It was such a different experience from going to church at Marchfold with Granny, which was an everyday thing, like brushing your teeth or washing your face.

The dawning of 1941 did not hold much encouragement, and as the year progressed the skies became ever darker.

Although we were beating the Italians in Abyssinia and Eritrea, elsewhere the Germans soon moved in and we were forced to retreat: first from Greece and then from Crete and then from along the North African Coast. The Nazis invaded the Balkans - Yugoslavia surrendered. Hitler boasted that the Third Reich would last for a thousand years. Millions of Jews were perishing all over Europe. The Germans called it 'The Final Solution'. They had other terrible plans for the future of mankind.

The Blitz continued to rage unabated over Britain. Liverpool and Plymouth were reduced to ruins. Huge landmines were dropped by parachute.

In the Atlantic, the convoys bringing supplies were occasionally attacked and casualties were heavy and mounting.

Hitler's deputy, Rudolf Hess, parachuted down from a crashed Messersmitt. He had been sent to make a deal.

My Diary:
Heard the cuckoo today and saw a swallow. I have started getting the garden ready for planting. Mr. Attwood has been doing the digging. I hope I have better luck this year. At least I'm not as ignorant as I was. I am going to grow lots of potatoes because the ones we bought during the winter had been frosted in store and tasted unpleasantly sweet and a little bad.

A new airfield is being built for Bomber Command, not five miles away from here at Marlington, and a second one within twenty miles.

Mr. Waring tries not to listen to the news. I expect it makes him think of his wife, and Violet stops her ears because she gets so upset.

I noticed that Mr. Waring had started to mumble to himself, but then I thought he had always mumbled. Then Violet said, "I'm terribly worried, Father is going about saying things to himself. At first I didn't really take any notice, but then I listened to what he was saying, and he's swearing under his breath - the most awful words."

I asked her what the words were and she said she couldn't possibly repeat them. She said she'd write them down, which she did. Some of them I had never heard of. They were a mixture of blasphemies and obscenities. I showed my mother the list and she said, "Poor man, he's distraught and angry. I should think it is quite a good way of getting rid of one's feelings - I must try it sometimes."

Violet tried to persuade her father to go with her to church, but he refused. I believe he never went again - certainly not while he was at Stunford. She made him go for walks with her when she took Johnie out in his pram. We started to play card games in the evenings to pass the time, and stop him from going to bed too early, and wandering about the house in the night.

Violet said, "I only hope Mrs. Attwood doesn't hear what Father is saying - or Maria for that matter."

My Diary:
The apple tree is in flower. I took Johnie and we sat under the branches and looked up through the blossom, which was buzzing with bees. Maria came and brought Bristles and put him in Johnie's pram. It's a good thing Violet didn't see. Johnie took fistfuls of Bristles' fur, but he didn't complain.

The apples that I wrapped in newspaper last year have been a godsend. Hardly any went bad and I have been making apple fool and stewed apples all winter. It was well worth the effort and I'm not sick of apples yet - I don't know about the others.

200,000 books were destroyed at the British Museum in the firebomb raid.

The wireless had been left on and for once Violet had listened. "The Germans have attacked the Russians," she told us. "I thought the Russians were their friends."

At first we imagined that she had got it wrong, but later discovered that it was true. It was difficult to believe.

My mother had two summer dresses made for Maria by the village sewing lady, Mrs. White. Mrs. White had worked at one time for a fashionable dressmaker in London. She told us this the first time we saw her, and within minutes of our meeting. Mrs. Attwood informed us that she was known to be a terrible gossip and was despised for the 'airs and graces' she affected.

We took Maria to an old-fashioned haberdashers shop in Banbury to choose the stuff. There were high stools to sit on at the varnished wood counters, and when you paid for your purchase the money was put into a container, which was then caterpaulted across the shop on a wire above our heads to disappear through a hole in the wall. The change and receipt made the same journey back.

The lady who served us was charmingly countrified and courteous. She brought bolts of printed cotton from shelves, dim in the back of the shop. When Maria was asked which ones she liked best, she would only say, "I don't mind," which was very annoying. In the end, a rosebud print and a blue flowery one were chosen. Maria nodded her head in approval.

When Mrs. White came to Chapel House a week later to try the dresses on her, Maria was obviously delighted and ran to my mother's bedroom to look at herself in the long mirror. When they were finished she wore them to school. One day, I found her crying uncontrollably in the garden. It was difficult to get her to tell me what the matter was. At school there was a big fat girl called Nora who had laughed at her, and shouted out across the playground that she looked 'more uglier than ever, even in her new dresses'.

We all told her how pretty she looked, Mrs. Attwood adding

that she looked "as pretty as a picture in a picture book," but I guess nothing could repair the damage, and the magic had gone. Mrs. White with her mouthful of pins had also played a part in this. "Aren't you a lucky girl to have the chance of living here and have people like this to buy you dresses?" she had said.

My Diary, 1st June:
Clothes are to be rationed - to be bought only with coupons. I am rather short of things to wear, because I have grown fatter in some places.
The potatoes are up. I go every morning early to see how they are doing. Everything is growing well - the broad beans and the runner beans. In fact, it looks like a proper vegetable garden. This year Maria and I made a scarecrow. I was tempted to use some of poor Mrs. Waring's clothes, but I would have had to ask Mr. Waring first, so I didn't. When it was finished, it looked horribly real, especially by moonlight.

So the summer passed, very slowly. Round about us was unbelievably beautiful, or so it seemed to me. There was so much blossom on the May trees that year, that they looked like white blobs. Everywhere pasture had been ploughed up to grow corn. Later, when it was ripe, the harvesters worked far into the night with lights.

* * * * *

The evenings were drawing in.

Mr. Waring went to my mother's bedroom door and knocked. She let him in.

"I've decided," he said, "to go and stay for a while with Auntie Jean (Mrs. Waring's sister). She has left London and taken a house in Devon. She's on her own, you see, and I could keep her company."

So Mr. Waring left. His son, Stephen, came and took him down to Devon. As he was leaving, he spoke almost inaudibly to my mother. "You have been remarkably kind to me, Mrs. Brocus,

165

and very understanding. I shall often think of you and Hannah. I hope you will be able to manage in these distressful circumstances and be able to help our Violet and our little Johnie. I know we had difficulties in the past, but you must realise that my very dear wife was very upset at the time."

When he'd gone, my mother said, "It's an extraordinary thing, but I find that it's possible to get fond of almost anybody."

CHAPTER 39

Violet had slowly made friends with Sylvia Havers and they went for walks together, pushing their prams. Once a week they both went to Banbury on the Thursday bus, leaving their babies with me to look after. They spent most of the day there and came back by taxi. The Havers' baby always struck me as being fat and stupid beside Johnie.

I sometimes wondered how they spent the time while they were out.

"Probably Violet does a thing called 'looking round the shops'," my mother said.

I pointed out that there were very few shops in Banbury to look round. "There's always Woolworths and Boots, and I expect they eat buns at the cake shop and drink tea."

My mother said, "I am so lucky to have Violet as a daughter-in-law. She really does love David and being so pretty she might well have wanted to gad about and have a good time while he's away. Loving him is a great bond between us, and nothing can change that."

My Diary, Sept. 17th:
Ian turned up today, out of the blue. We couldn't believe our eyes. He brought us stockings, butter, coffee, sugar and biscuits. Violet told me that she heard his voice in the hall and for one moment thought it was David miraculously returned. Their voices are very alike.

He stayed for a week. Emotionally it was very draining, as all the time we were dreading the day he had to go.

He busied himself doing all sorts of jobs that needed doing about the house, and he did things to the car.

His leave went all too quickly for us, but not, I think, for him. He had had enough of his mother's fussing and Violet's sad yearning presence.

Maria fell in love with him and sat dumbfounded in his company. He teased and played with her. I could see that it was painful for her.

It was shortly after this that Maria's Auntie Katalina turned up - a big boxer of a woman, with a thick neck and great arms - and took her away. We never found out why. Maria cried when she left, just as she had cried when she came. I cried too, but after she'd gone.

My mother picked up Bristles and went to her bedroom. I went and sat under the apple tree.

I wrote to her several times, but she never wrote back. I suppose it was too difficult. I enclosed a stamped addressed envelope once, but I never heard.

Mr. Havers asked Violet if she would like to teach in the Sunday School. She was pleased and flattered. It helped her to make a shape to her week. In this way she got to know people in the village who had children. At first she was able to take Johnie with her, but as he grew disruptive and mobile, she had to leave him at home.

My Diary, 27th Sept:
It is time to pick the apples again. Last year seems so long ago. I shall soon be 19. I have been tidying up the garden and clearing away all the dead stuff. There are still some runner beans left.

It was the middle of the night when I heard a great noise coming from Violet's bedroom. I jumped out of bed and ran to see what the matter was. There was Violet standing in the middle of her room, the whole place in complete turmoil. All the drawers had been pulled out and everything thrown around: clothes were hanging out of the cupboard. Johnie had woken up and was crying.

"I've lost a letter, a special letter from David," she said, "I've just got to have it."

I tried to calm her. "Where did you last have it?" I asked, but she was almost incoherent.

My mother appeared. She tried to reason with Violet.

"Just take a deep breath," she coaxed. "Leave everything as it is and go to bed and in the morning we'll go through it all, bit by bit. It's impossible to find anything in this light."

This made Violet even worse. "I've just got to have it, don't you understand?" she kept saying. So we went on looking. I didn't even know what it looked like. After about an hour, I thought of pulling the bed out, and there it was - the letter, lodged between the wall and the bed.

Thankfully, some sort of order was restored and we all went back to bed. I lay awake though listening to Johnie, who didn't go to sleep but insisted on playing until dawn.

Chapter 40

My Diary:
We had a letter from Ian. In it he told us that he was going to get married to a girl called Ann Shelton. He said as soon as they could get leave together, he would bring her to see us. She was in the WAAF.

This was something of a bombshell, as you can imagine. Mrs. Attwood said, "I expect she meant to have him."

It wasn't long before Ian brought Ann to see us. They turned up in an old red sports car. She was very nice and easy to talk to, and we liked her very much. They seemed to be very much in love. They wanted to get married as soon as it could be arranged. The wedding was going to be in church and nobody except the family would be invited.

During their visit we gleaned that Ann's father had died and her mother had remarried a retired soldier and landowner in Northamptonshire, a Colonel Betterstone. He lived in the village of Melton. We also gathered that she didn't get on very well with him.

As soon as we knew the date of the wedding, we wrote to the Aunts, hoping that some of them would be able to come.

A letter came from Ann to my mother. She wrote:

'You don't know how lucky I feel to be going to marry Ian. It is easy to be frightened with all that we are involved in, but I hope I will be a loving support for him and not too clinging - it won't be easy.

I very much enjoyed meeting you and Hannah, Violet and Johnie. Chapel House is so friendly.

I am going to wear my mother's wedding dress. It fits perfectly, which is surprising. The silk down one side is slightly discoloured, but I don't think it will matter and I am going to wear the veil that my grandmother had.

I hope it won't be too difficult for you to get to Melton.

I'm afraid it may be a tiresome journey.
        With love to you all from
                Ann'

When it came to dress up for the wedding, I found that I had grown out of almost all my clothes. There was an awful stretching of gaps and gaping of buttons. I didn't want to use my clothes coupons buying something that I wasn't going to wear all the time, so I asked Violet if I could borrow something of hers. After much trying on and deliberation, she kindly lent me a blue dress. Unfortunately, it was made of rather thin stuff for the time of year, but really there was no choice.

Then there was the question of hats. Violet had lots of hats. "Help yourself," she said. But her head was larger than mine and they all fell down over my nose. We decided to go to the shop in Banbury where we had bought Maria the material for her summer dresses. The lady assistant asked kindly after her. We told her that she had been taken back to London.

Seeing myself in the looking-glass in the shop was not encouraging. Despair was setting in when my mother decided on a rather drastic straw with a wide brim. "That really looks nice, Hannah," she said. She later decorated it with loops of Petersham ribbon.

Violet wasn't at all keen on going to the wedding, but my mother persuaded her, explaining that we really needed her.

"Johnie will cry in the church," she protested. "I know he will, and what about the journey?"

The journey was not far, but it was complicated. The village taxi had to take us all the way to Brackley to get on the right line, where we caught the train for Northampton. From Northampton Station we had to get another taxi to Melton. I thought we looked like a party of Gypsies on the move with all Johnie's equipment - clean nappies, bottles, etc. and his pushchair. Our finery too, by early morning winter light, didn't help either. Violet had made a great effort. She was dressed in a green silk outfit with a big hat, curled round the brim with ostrich feathers. She wore very high heels, which made progress hazardous - especially when she was carrying Johnie.

My mother had dug out a grey dress for the occasion, which she hadn't worn for years. Why it should have looked quite so nice, I don't know, but it did. With it she wore a grey silk beret with Granny Bell's diamond brooch pinned on the front.

When we left Brackley Station Johnie was pristine and shining clean, but when we arrived at Northampton, he was smudged and smeared with black. The smoke from the engine had blown into the compartment and we had difficulty pulling the window up. There was no heating in the train and it had turned out to be a very cold day, as we had feared.

We arrived at Paxton Place in good time. It was a large farmhouse, standing in the middle of fields, surrounded by a beautiful high garden wall.

We were greeted by Ann's mother, a taut woman with immaculately done hair. She cast a sweeping glance over us and what she saw evidently didn't encourage her. As a result she treated us with great condescension - you could even say, disdain.

She introduced us to Colonel Betterstone, a small, erect little man with a high voice. He rather took to Violet and never missed an opportunity of talking to her during the day.

Inside the house, the long low rooms were sparsely, but valuably, furnished. The white walls were hung with family pictures.

My mother whispered: "What a lovely house; what a lovely place."

I took her arm. "It's not nearly as nice as Marchfold," I said.

"It depends on what you want," she replied, "and anyway, Marchfold doesn't exist anymore."

We got a fleeting glimpse of the bride in her wedding dress as she slipped across the upstairs landing.

Violet had to go quickly to try and restore Johnie's appearance. None of our family had come, so we felt very downcast and outnumbered. We put in time by standing in front of the big log fire in the hall, trying to get warm, while around us guests kept arriving and women helpers from the village hurried to and fro, making last minute preparations for the wedding meal.

A woman approached my mother and upset her very much. "How do you feel about wartime marriages? Personally, I disapprove strongly. I nearly didn't come. I know they did everything they could to try and dissuade Ann. They should have waited until after the war. I understand that he is a bomber pilot, and that makes it even worse. Not a very good prospect to have to face the world on your own with a baby."

My mother turned away. There wasn't really anything she could say. We never discovered who the woman was, or what connection she had with the family.

When it was time to leave for the service, various people's cars were there to take us. We went with Colonel Betterstone's mother, a formidable presence, tall and white-haired, dressed in a long mink coat. After acknowledging our existence, I do not think she spoke another word to us.

The small old church was just outside the village. Round it grew tall leafless elm trees.

When we arrived, we were overjoyed to find Vanessa, Uncle Donald, May and Kate standing in the porch. Reinforcements had arrived, just in time to relieve the beleaguered Brocus's.

"All was not lost, you see," my mother said as we got out of the car.

There was a very ugly marble tomb in the church, a 19th century monument to one of the dead Betterstones. There was, of course, no heating. Ian was already standing by the altar, with his best man. A man we had never met, both of them were in uniform. Because of the cold, their breath was condensing around them as they breathed.

The bride arrived: she walked up the aisle on the arm of her stepfather - she was taller than he.

Afterwards my mother said, "I thought she looked so lovely in her white dress, but when she stood beside Ian, it was too much to bear." We were all hopelessly moved, but fortunately our feelings were stifled by having to make Johnie be quiet. He started to make a noise and when we tried to stop him, he began to cry loudly.

174

After the service ended, Ian and Ann walked down the aisle together and, as they stepped out into the churchyard, a watery winter sun shone on them.

The lady organist had made a lot of mistakes in her playing, but the Vicar explained that the usual organist had, unfortunately, been called up only a week before.

Back at the house, we filed into the dining-room for the wedding breakfast.

The Aunts were exploding with emotion. All of us seemed stunned and tearful. Ian was very quiet and serious; Violet was silent; Johnie disruptive.

The meal was surprisingly good. There was meat in a nice sauce. Fortunately, I didn't realise until afterwards that it was rabbit. We had champagne.

When it came to Ian's turn to speak, he got up and said, "I'm not going to make a proper speech, you'll be glad to hear. I just want to thank Col. Betterstone and my mother-in-law for putting on such a wonderful show for us in such difficult times, and to thank everyone for turning up. To marry Ann is the best thing that has ever happened to me in the whole of my life - that, and flying. I know she'll understand me saying that, because she knows."

Ann looked down at her hands.

The wedding cake was not elaborate, but there was enough to go round, and some left over to send to relatives who were not able to come.

My Diary, 8th December:
Ian's wedding yesterday. I would have liked a second piece of cake, but I didn't get the chance. Aunt May came back home with us. She is an ambulance driver in Coventry now. Today I took her to Banbury and put her on the train for Leamington.

175

CHAPTER 41

My Diary, 9th Dec.:
The Japanese have attacked the Americans at a place called Pearl Harbour - it happened without warning. They say now the Americans will have to join with us in fighting the war and that everything will be different.

My Diary, 12th December:
My birthday. Far from the war coming to an end, it has intensified and spread and got worse and worse and worse.

My mother had a letter from a friend of David's called John Peterson. He was one of the crowd of boys who came from school to our summer tennis and tea parties. We remembered that he had started off in the choir school, was very musical and played the piano brilliantly. When we saw him last, he had just decided to give up everything and concentrate on his music.

He asked for David's address. My mother wrote to him telling him that David had been posted abroad and was probably somewhere in the Far East.

An answer to her letter came by return of post. It said:

'I have been in the Merchant Navy now for about eight months. I am on leave at the moment, after being torpedoed in the Atlantic, and am now waiting for another ship. I am looking up old friends to fill in the time. My own family has been hopelessly scattered by the war, so I have no base at all to go back to.'

My mother answered at once, inviting him to come and stay with us for as long as ever he wanted. A few days later he turned up.

We did just recognise him, in spite of his appalling appearance. He was terribly gaunt and thin. We discovered that he had only just come out of hospital, after being adrift for days on a life raft at sea.

He was terribly restless.

"I've made a terrible mistake asking him here," my mother

177

said. "It's hopeless for him to be in a house full of women with nothing to do. We haven't even got a piano."

We introduced him to the Havers, thinking that Mr. Havers would take an interest in him and encourage him in some way, which he didn't. They did have an old piano which they allowed him to play. He went once or twice, but it was out of tune and not all the notes worked. He said it was impossible and didn't go again. We took him to see the Misses Bates and Professor and Mrs. Reicht in the hope that talking to the Professor and his wife might help.

One night he woke up shouting and yelling. We all staggered out of our sleep to his room. It was difficult to calm him down, and frightening.

After he had been with us for two weeks, it became obvious that he had fallen violently in love with Violet. It was my mother's awful task to tell him he must leave.

It was unbelievably dreadful - completely unbearable.

He left his watch behind and no address.

Mrs. Attwood underlined our despair by saying, "Y'm done your best - y'm can't do no more."

CHAPTER 42

It was Christmas Day 1941. We had hoped that Ian and Ann would have been able to come, but they couldn't. We invited the two Misses Bates, the Professor and his wife and the Havers to join us for lunch.

In the event, only Sylvia Havers and her baby came. The Bates' household were all in various stages of influenza. The Reverend Havers was too busy with his services, and Mrs. Havers had to stay at home with their dog because he had diarrhoea.

I remember how much I missed Maria, and wondered what she was doing and where she was.

I had managed to get two big chickens. I'm afraid they were rather tough.

Violet and Sylvia drank too much sherry and became silly. Johnie sat up at the table and threw his food on the floor. The other baby sat on her mother's lap doing the same thing. Bristles and Rubby cleared it up. It was a funny sort of celebration.

The news was that Hong Kong had surrendered to the Japanese.

My Diary:
Violet went to visit the Havers yesterday. It was New Year's Eve. There, staying on leave, was their son Andrew. She said he spoke about seeing Ian in Canada, and suggested that he might come over and see us, but he didn't.

12th Jan, 1942:
Kuala Lumpur has fallen to the Japanese.

This came as a great shock to us, because Kuala Lumpur is where we lived and where my father worked for thirty years.

Although I was very young when we left, I remembered it vividly. Our house stood two or three miles on the plain outside the town. The distance was rimmed by far-off hills, faintly blue. The two-storey building was open to the tropical air, except for our bedrooms which were enclosed by fine meshed wire, against the mosquitos. On the shaded steps that led up to the house, there were tall ferns growing in pots. In them the ever-fluttering rice birds built their nests.

My father had planted a beautiful garden full of trees and brilliant flowers. The toc-toc bird made his monotonous call, all day long, and the frogs clamoured after the rain in the cool of the night. The darkness was full of the chirruping of insects and terrible cries, and the constant sound of dripping after a storm.

In our hall, leaning against the wall at the back, was a heavy rickshaw-shaft. My father wrested it from a man who was using it to beat his wife. Thereafter, he kept it to hand to repel intruders.

One night, we were all awakened by the most fearful screams. Father leapt from his bed, seized the rickshaw shaft and rushed out into the night, but was unable to find the cause.

In the morning, the servants told us what had happened. A Chinese man had had his ears cut off in a dispute.

Every evening at the same time, a bullock cart carrying the dead from the hospital went past on its way to the cemetery, its wooden wheels grinding and wobbling laboriously along the dusty road in the stifling heat. The smell was bad because the contractor had cheated and made the coffins too short for the bodies. In many cases, the feet stuck out beneath the lids. My father had continuous trouble with the coffin-makers and the grave-diggers. The grave-diggers didn't dig proper graves, and the bodies were chucked out of the coffins into the ground, and coffins were used time and time again. To avoid detection, they took to using only the lids.

One of our diversions as children were the Chinese funeral processions that went past the end of the drive. Tremendously noisy and colourful, they clanged and wailed their way along. On these occasions, sometimes David used to shout, "let's show off!" and, I'm ashamed to say, we used to rush down to the gate shouting and yelling and waving our arms and legs about as they went by. Once, we put our tongues out.

And now, the Japanese Army was there - marching through

all the memories in my head - actually in those very places we'd been in.

"I'm glad your father isn't here to see this day," my mother said.

We tried not to think too much about it.

CHAPTER 43

By this time Johnie was beginning to talk. He could say 'Mama' and 'Hani' and 'Gran'. All the animals he called 'gagas', including Bristles and Rubby. Every day Violet showed him a photograph of David and said, "Say Daddy, Daddy; say nigh' nigh' Daddy'.

One night Johnie made a grab at the photograph and crumpled and tore it. Violet shouted, "Don't do that!" and hit him right across the face. Johnie let out all his breath and was silent for a split second, before giving out a great shocked cry.

Violet wailed, "What have I done? What have I done? Johnie, forgive me, forgive me, what would your Daddy say? What would David say?" She snatched Johnie up into her arms, hugging and rocking him. Both of them were sobbing. A deep red mark appeared on Johnie's cheek and across his nose.

My mother heard the commotion and came running. "Whatever has happened?" she asked breathlessly. "Whatever is the matter?"

"I hit Johnie - God forgive me - I've never done it before and I hope I never do it again!" We were all shaken.

I wrote in my Diary that day:
Violet smacked Johnie hard - all of us were upset.

Sylvia Havers told Violet that her brother Andrew had been married for several years to a girl called Muriel. Trouble arose when she objected to him joining the Air Force. She left him just before he went to Canada.

No one is supposed to know about it, which seems to me to be rather silly. Mrs. Havers terribly doesn't want it to get round the village. Sylvia went on to tell Violet that they had never cared much for Muriel. She was rather 'fast' and inclined to be extravagant, and was always completely bored at the Vicarage, thinking up wild things to do, which shocked the village. I would like to know what the 'wild things' were.

The first American troops have arrived in this country.

My Diary, Tuesday 10th February:
Mrs. Attwood is upset because soap is going to be rationed - four ounces of household soap or soapflakes per month, per person. This will affect her little washing and ironing business. She will only be able to carry on if customers give her some of their soap ration with the laundry.

My Diary, 16th February:
Yesterday, Singapore surrendered to the Japanese. The terrible question now is how will they treat the 130,000 prisoners that they have taken there?

No letters came from David for a while. Then a whole lot arrived together. After that there were no more. Every morning Violet ran downstairs in her nightdress with bare feet, when she heard the postman come. At that time of the year it was as cold inside the house as out. She went on doing it for months - long after the letters stopped coming.

Violet found an old wind-up gramophone amongst Ian's things and a pile of records. She got it out and started to play the records. She played her favourites over and over again. You could hear her winding the handle. Sometimes she went on doing it all day, only stopping for meals.

My Diary, 28th February:
Things continue to go very badly in the Far East. But, the Germans are in trouble in the snow in Russia.

About this time, for me, there was the first glimmer of hope:

A minister has been appointed to be in charge of Post War Planning. Obviously, some people must expect the War to come to a victorious end one day. I find it hard to believe. You can't carry out plans for the future if you're beaten, so they must expect us to win.

CHAPTER 44

My Diary, Saturday, 14th March:
Violet had a letter from David's Regiment, saying that he was missing. It said: 'According to information now received, your husband was serving in Malaya when the Garrison of Singapore capitulated on the 15th February 1942. Every endeavour is being made through diplomatic and other channels to obtain information concerning him, and it is hoped that he is safe, although he may be a prisoner of war. Immediately any further information is obtained, it will be sent to you from this office, but, in the meantime, it is regretted that it is necessary to post him as 'missing'. Should you yourself receive any information from any source regarding your husband dated later than 15th February, I would be most grateful if you could inform us at once, stating all particulars.'
We had all been expecting it.

There was one on the same day from the War Office. It said:
'It is with regret that I have to notify you that on 15th February 1942 your husband was reported missing.' It then went on to tell her that her family allowance would continue.

When Violet read the letter, she stood in the hall and started to scream. My mother came out of her bedroom and said, "Whatever is the matter?" When she heard the reason, she went back into her room and shut the door.

Violet went on screaming. I couldn't think what to do or how to stop her. In the end she fell on the floor, without breath. Johnie was beginning to walk by this time, and had crawled up the kitchen steps and over to his mother, where he started to pull her clothes. I picked him up and took him out into the garden, although it was cold. There were cows in the field. "Look at the cows," I said, pointing. His sobbing gradually subsided into snatched breaths.

That night I slept with my mother. We lay side by side in the dark, hour after hour. Towards dawn, I heard Violet being sick. She had taken a whole bottle of aspirins, which made her violently ill. I got her settled somehow, and then took Johnie with me to my own bed. He clung to me with the tenacity of survival, spreading warmth and comfort to the centre of my being. His head was wet with Violet's tears.

In the morning, I took my mother her kettle. She made no effort to get up and lay there all day. Violet could hardly stand after taking the aspirins. I told her to stay lying down until she felt better. I looked after Johnie. I took him in his pushchair to the Post Office. I had to send a telegram to Ian, telling him what had happened. In the evening, after putting Johnie to bed, I went and sat with my mother. "You've got to keep going," I said, "because of Johnie." She didn't answer. After a while I asked her if she had heard. "Oh, yes, I heard," she replied. "I'll try." She stayed in bed for a whole week.

Violet cried all day, every day.

When I thought about my brother and Violet, my sadness and fear became so intense that I got stomach cramps.

We had known all along that David was on his way to the Far East, and when Singapore fell, we really knew what must have happened to him, but we hoped and prayed silently that perhaps he hadn't arrived before the surrender, or that some miracle had kept him safe.

The realisation of our worst fears was hard. I wrote to the Aunts to tell them.

The Vicar arrived to comfort Violet, but she hid. He couldn't even talk to my mother because she was in bed. He spoke to me of the gnawing anxieties that his wife was suffering now that their son Andrew was flying with Bomber Command and going on bombing missions over Germany.

My Diary, 2nd April:
The Vicar came. He didn't stay long, thank goodness. Bristles is so good, the way he lets Johnie catch hold of great tufts of his fur and pull his whiskers.

I will try and see if I can get some coke ... If we could all have a bath, it would be good, I think. Mrs. Attwood has been kindly and helpful to my mother.

5th April:
Ian came on his own and stayed one night. He persuaded Mother to get up.

Violet doesn't seem to get dressed, nor does she undress at night. She just has things on. It doesn't look as though she's done her hair, either.

Ian's presence was very comforting. He had a talk with Violet. I don't know what he said to her, but she seemed a lot better afterwards and went and smartened herself up. He took me into the garden and told me that Ann was expecting a baby. "It's what we both wanted," he said. "Will you promise me that if I'm killed, you won't ever lose track of her?" I remember being furious with him for using the word 'killed'. He could have said, 'If something happens to me,' or 'In wartime you can never tell what's going to happen.' Anyway, I was so horrified that at first I couldn't speak, but did manage at last to say, "of course."

"Don't tell Mother about Ann yet. I'll tell her myself in a little while."

I asked him what Ann did, and he told me she was a 'plotter'. "She means to keep going till she's seven months at least," he said.

Before he left he put a new washer on one of the bathroom taps. I watched carefully so that I would know how to do it myself.

CHAPTER 45

My mother made a great effort and we went to London to look at the house. Because of how Violet was feeling, we got Sylvia Havers to come and stay with her while we were away.

We got a taxi from Paddington. London looked dirty and battered. We found the house pock-marked with shrapnel from the ack-ack guns in the park. A lot of the ornamental stucco had fallen off and windows were broken. The other houses in the street looked much the same.

Inside the house we discovered that all the rooms were stacked with peoples' belongings from bombed-out houses.

While we were standing in the hall surveying the desolation, a man opened the front door with a key and walked in.

"I'm fire-watching tonight," he said. "What are you doing here?"

My mother replied that it was her house.

"I suppose you're one of those people who left London when the bombing started and live in every luxury in the country - not even having to stick to food rationing properly. I expect you don't even realise that there is a war on!"

My mother sat down on the bottom step of the stairs. I looked away. "Oh well," he said, "I came for my thermos flask. I'll get it and be off."

There didn't seem any point in saying anything. He went and, presently, we left too.

My Diary, Mon. 6th April:
Violet asked me if I would write to her father and to her brother to tell them the bad news. Which I did.

When Aunt May got my letter telling her about David, she went straight to Leamington Station and caught a train to Banbury. On arrival she found that there were no taxis, so she started to walk, thinking that she might be lucky and get a lift. But no one came past, and by the time she got to Stunford it was already dark. I opened the door to her. "I haven't walked so far in years," she said, gasping. Certainly eight miles is quite a distance for anybody. It had been raining and her face and hair were glistening wet. My mother was overwhelmed when she saw her. Aunt May stayed the night and went back the next afternoon.

Violet said, "Fancy your Aunt walking all that distance. I'm sure I could never do it. After all, she's not that young, is she?"

I could see the next day that Aunt May was extremely stiff, but when I enquired, she wouldn't admit to the slightest discomfort.

My Diary, 13th April:
Granny Bell's birthday. Heard the cuckoo. Violet put her hands over her ears and said, "I don't want to hear that dreadful sound. Johnie is teething".

The month of May passed. After we heard that David was missing, my mother didn't listen to the news on the wireless for a long time, or only very seldom. She couldn't bear to hear what the Japanese were doing in the East, raiding and capturing all the islands in the Pacific, and bombing and sinking our ships in the Indian Ocean. She couldn't manage to listen either to how many of our planes had not returned from raids over Germany. She was sure that Ian must have taken part in the 1,000 bomber raid on Cologne.

My Diary, Monday 15th June:
Sylvia Havers' husband is in North Africa. The news from there is far from good. She appears to have such a sunny personality that nothing seems to worry her unduly. Mrs. Havers walked over with her son Andrew. They stayed and had some tea. He is very good-looking and just as nice as Ian said he was. He played with Johnie and chatted easily with Violet and my mother, and stroked Rubby's ears.

That is all I wrote in my diary about Andrew Havers, but in fact the moment that I set eyes on him, I fell violently in love with him. At the time I had very little else to occupy my mind, so it became an all-enveloping obsession. I remember it was called being 'love sick'. I certainly was, and accepted the fact that I just had to put up with it, but, as well as being painful, it was exciting and gave a new meaning and colour to the world around me. I resolved never to let anyone know about it, even if it killed me. I was afraid that he would never really even notice me, but I kept myself going on hopes and dreams. My fantasies were made even more remote by hearing from Sylvia that his wife Muriel had unexpectedly turned up at the Vicarage the very evening of the day he had visited us. She said she wanted to have another try at being married to him, and further said that if he didn't have her back she would kill herself. He succumbed to the threat. Sylvia said, "He really shouldn't have to put up with this emotional turmoil at this time. He won't be able to cope with it."

My Diary, Sunday, 21st June:
Violet's brother came for the weekend. They both went to early service. It has been a lovely day. Stephen says that their father is much better. He has joined the Home Guard where he is living. What would Mrs. Waring say if she got to hear about it? Probably, 'He that lives by the sword, shall perish by the sword.' In this case, probably his own sword.

We shall have new potatoes before long now - they look very good.

The Germans have taken 35,000 prisoners after capturing Tobruk? I wonder if Sylvia's husband is amongst them?

8th July:
Violet heard from the Vicarage that Andrew's wife has insisted on renting a cottage near to the airfield where he is stationed. This is much frowned on, because having wives and families living so close puts extra strain on the men engaged in operations.

This was indeed the case - wives living near to their husband's

191

bases, dreaded the orders that sent them off into the night on missions deep into enemy territory, and agonised through the dark hours waiting to hear of their safe return.

This tension undermined the morale of men carrying heavy responsibilities and suffering enormous strain anyway.

I thought about Andrew and knew how different I would be if I were his wife. Not selfish and demanding, but quietly devoted and supportive, as I imagined Ann to be.

That summer I spent a lot of time with Johnie under the apple tree. He played with earth and stones, and I dreamed the time away thinking of Andrew.

I felt guilty. Things were so bad. Violet was only just surviving, like a lot of other people.

My mother sat with Bristles on her lap all day. When she wasn't sitting, she seemed to be carrying him about.

My Diary, 30th July:
There was an advertisement in the paper for stone-ground wholemeal flour, by the sack. It came today. I opened the bag. It looks as though it is going to be very good for us. It feels in the hand like sand and smells of sacking. I shall make steamed puddings when we have some fat, and dumplings.

14th August:
I can feel the days drawing in again, ever so slightly. It almost feels like a threat.

We heard from Ian. Ann had been very ill and it seemed likely that she might be invalided out of the WAAF. She is staying with her mother at the moment, but he said he was trying to find a place for her to live, nearer to where he is stationed.

I never heard anything more about the baby and I didn't mention it to my mother. I knew Ann had had a miscarriage.

That year I remember was a very good blackberry year. I couldn't make jam because there was no sugar. I picked pounds and pounds and bottled them more or less successfully. They made

192

a welcome change, mixed with our constant stewed apple and apple snow, during the coming winter.

My Diary, 31st August:
We have made a landing on the French coast at Dieppe. Our first attempt to gain a foothold on the Continent again. The landing was carried out by Canadians. It was disaster from start to finish. The troops were slaughtered on the beaches and cliffs. The official line is that we had no intention of staying; that it was only a probe of the enemy's defences and that we were going to withdraw anyway after a short period of time.

After this, I see that I didn't write in my diary for a while. Early in September Ian was posted as missing. his plane failed to return after a raid over Germany. We were quite unprepared for this new blow.

My mother said, "I never thought I would lose both my sons." She had made up her mind that they were dead.

I was doing the kettles one morning, when Sylvia came, out of breath, from the Vicarage. Andrew had crash-landed his bomber after returning from a raid over Germany. Only one member of his crew had been killed, but Andrew's face and hands had been badly burnt. Mr. and Mrs. Havers were going at once to see him in hospital.

Making Johnie the excuse, I went and sat under the apple tree. He had a special game he played there with pebbles.

CHAPTER 46

It was November - winter again.

It was my birthday. I was twenty. I looked at myself in the glass: "I look old already," I said aloud.

I had to go into Banbury to register for National Service. David's arrangements took effect and I was exempted, to my utter frustration.

We heard that Andrew's wife had already left him again, only a short time before he crashed. She didn't like the house he had found for her to live in, and he was never there when she wanted to be taken out or go to parties. Things went from bad to worse and in a very short time she took herself off again.

My Diary, 5th November:
Mrs. Havers came back from seeing Andrew in hospital. She told us she had been to his rented cottage and tried to sort things out, so that he didn't have to go back there and face it all when he came out.

If this isn't enough for the poor Havers to be going on with, their ghastly dog has just died.

Sylvia regularly has letters from her husband in North Africa. Sometimes she reads them out to poor Violet.

There are dreadful stories about what the Japanese are doing, and awful things are happening to the Jews in Warsaw.

We saw the Bates, who told us the Reichs have got their permits to go to America and expect to be leaving during the next three months or so.

A nephew of the Bates is in the Navy and he has just got back from sailing with a convoy to Nurmansk. It was so dreadful and the losses so catastrophic in the icy sea that he has been given a month's leave.

The tide really does seem to be turning in North Africa: the news is actually good.

CHAPTER 47

It was well into December before Ann heard that Ian was a prisoner of war in Germany.

My mother and I could hardly believe it. It was too good to be true. We were ill with relief.

At supper that night Violet had an outburst.

She yelled, "I suppose you're both so delighted that Ian's alive that you hardly even bother to remember that David ever existed!" She leapt up from the table crying and rushed out of the room, banging the door so hard that the house shook. Johnie, who hadn't yet gone to bed, started to scream. Supper was deserted and wasted. I cleared away and washed up and then took Johnie up to bed with me. I heard the sirens go off somewhere in the distance.

During the night, Violet came and snatched Johnie up in a sort of rage and took him to her room, banging the doors behind her.

It was just before Christmas that Andrew left hospital and came back to the Vicarage. I was relieved to see that his face wasn't in any way disfigured, but patchy and red down one side. It certainly didn't look burnt. One of his hands was badly scarred and the other was still covered and in a sling.

My Diary, 27th December:
We had a Christmas tree for Johnie. I made coloured paper chains and hung them from the beams in the kitchen, and I decorated the whole house with holly and ivy. The Aunts sent him presents and we enjoyed seeing him unwrap them.

Violet was very low. My mother gave her one of her pieces of jewellery - a pearl and sapphire pendant on a little gold chain. She was very delighted and gave my mother a kiss.

Mrs. Attwood gave us four pork chops from a pig they had just killed. We gave her some money. The sun shone.

We walked over to the Vicarage for lunch and heard the King's Christmas message on the wireless afterwards. We were all moved by it. His halting words seemed to symbolise unreasonable courage in adversity.

Andrew walked back home with us and stayed until supper time. Johnie showed him his new toys.

We started to talk about the Germans in the Russian winter at Stalingrad and Leningrad. My mother said, "It's extraordinary that Hitler actually thought he could succeed where Napoleon failed - perhaps he hasn't read his history properly or doesn't know about the cold."

My Diary, 1st January 1943:

I try not to think too much about David - then when I do try to think of him, I can't. Violet seems to be pulling herself together a little. I took her and my mother to Banbury. Violet bought a pair of warm slacks with her coupons. They are check brown and green. My mother goes to a woman tailor who works from her own house. She has just had a skirt made out of some tweed she had put by. Miss Arden (the tailoress) told her that several of her young customers, recently widowed, had brought their husband's trousers to her to be unpicked and made up into skirts. 'Very successful they've been' she said. 'The ladies have been very pleased with the results.'

Ann wrote and asked us if she could come and stay for a while. Thereafter she came and went until the end of the war. I think when Chapel House became intolerable, she went back to her mother and stepfather, and when they became unbearable, she left them and came to us.

The advent of Andrew and Ann greatly changed our tedious lives, even if it didn't improve them. The first time Ann came to stay, she looked very ill. She hadn't fully recovered from her miscarriage. Her clothes hung on her in folds. In spite of feeling unwell, she never let herself go, and occupied herself sewing or knitting or helping in the house or in the garden, but she brought with her new tensions. She obviously found Violet very trying, but hardly ever said anything aloud. Her silent censure flustered Violet and made her say even sillier things than usual. Perhaps Ann was a little jealous of Violet's looks.

Violet, in her turn, found Ann's self-containment very exasperating - also Ann heated her own kettle, which was a reproach.

Andrew made a habit of coming to see us nearly every day, but some days he went off for walks, leaving the Vicarage in the morning and often not returning until well after dark. Sometimes, Mrs. Havers got worried at the length of time he had been away. I noticed that he had days of black despair, when he hardly spoke. Everyone put it down to his crash. I thought it was because of his wife. He told us that he found his injured hands very frustrating, "I'd spend my time sorting out the sheds at the Vicarage, if I could," he said, "or tidying the paths, but I can't. Having bad hands makes me very self-centred and sorry for myself, but when I think of what other people have to face up to, I'm ashamed. This really is a wonderful opportunity for me to read all the books that I ought to have read. There are enough books at the Vicarage to last a lifetime." He tried to sound enthusiastic.

Sylvia used to bring her fat Theresa to play with Johnie, and we all took to playing cards to pass the time in the dark winter evenings of early 1943, when the wind blew the branches of the yew tree against the kitchen window.

Ann had a little wireless. She listened to it in her bedroom. Our mealtimes were slightly more lively, now that Ann was staying. She was obviously used to making conversation and she took trouble to include Violet, however annoying she found her. When Andrew stayed to supper, which he often did, the company was more balanced and easier. On this occasion, Andrew had gone back to hospital to have something done to his hand, and we were sitting round the kitchen table having supper. Ann said, "The Germans are in full retreat from Stalingrad, isn't that wonderful news, and we've made our first daylight raids on Berlin."

Violet put her knife and fork down and looked at Ann.

"I think it's wicked the way we are bombing the Germans. We should stop it and apologise for what we have done. I can't see why we couldn't have given Hitler what he wanted in the first place.

If we had, none of these dreadful things would have happened to us."

My mother burst out, "What about the concentration camps, and the Jews in Warsaw and elsewhere, and other prisoners like Ian - shouldn't we batter at Germany till they're freed?"

"I expect the Jews brought it on themselves," Violet replied. "Anyway, I suppose we're all guilty. Let him that is blameless cast the first stone."

Poor Violet, her head was full of texts (many of which she got wrong). Every now and then one would pop out meaningless and irrelevant in the most unsuitable circumstances.

It was about this time that I noticed that Violet had let her appearance go somewhat. Strangely enough, it made her look even more vulnerable and appealing.

My Diary, 17th February:
Violet's brother has at last succeeded in getting out of the Fire Service and into the Army. He wrote to Violet - reading between the lines, she understands that he is training in Northern Ireland.

Ann told my mother that she was hoping very much to be able to go back into the WAAF, and she said to me, 'Waiting for Ian would be so much easier if I was working, and besides I would feel I was really doing something worthwhile.'

Mrs. Attwood is a great admirer of Ann.

The garden looks a dreary mud patch. It's difficult to believe that it will ever grow anything again or sprout up. There is rain and a strong wind from the Bristol Channel.

I don't know what made Violet leave off playing the gramophone.

When Andrew came out of hospital again after his operation, he went up to Scotland to stay with a friend's parents. We didn't see him again until the worst of the winter was over.

28th February:
The aconites are out.

Ann has gone back home.

Mrs. Attwood brought us an awful rabbit. I made it into a pie; I haven't had a rabbit since Ian's wedding.

Johnie is such a lovely little boy. He has grown so much and his talking has come on such a lot, quite unlike Theresa who does not utter a word - only eats.

Violet doesn't talk to Johnie about David anymore, but

he is still mentioned every night in bedtime prayers.

Got some lavatory paper from the shop today - it came from under the counter and was whipped into my basket before anyone saw it.

15th March:
Andrew has come back to the Vicarage. He hasn't been over yet. It isn't dry enough to start working in the garden. I heard a blackbird this morning.

Sunday 21st March:
Andrew walked over to see us. Violet was at church when he came. He looked much better. He says he can't wait to get back to flying. 'Mooching around with nothing to do is enough to get anyone down. I want to get on with it,' he said.

So time went slowly by - I was dreading Andrew going away again. Violet announced that she was going to take Andrew's advice. He had told her how good long strenuous walks were for the spirits: a wonderful antidote to depression and morbid fancies. "While he's here, I shall join him," she said. "That is, if you will very kindly look after Johnie while I'm out. When he goes back, I shall have to keep it up on my own, which won't be much fun."

At first, she wasn't away too long, but the walks got longer and longer. I felt jealous of her being with Andrew and resentful about being left with Johnie.

Mrs. Attwood voiced disapproval and hinted at talk in the village. My mother was surprised by what Mrs. Attwood said, and replied to it by saying, "Violet is a really good girl. We don't need to worry about her. If people in the village want to say silly things, it can't be helped."

Certainly walking did appear to do her the world of good. She started to take an interest in her appearance once again and be more patient with Johnie. She was also kinder to my mother and more considerate to me.

I was glad when Ann came back to stay.

My Diary, 12th April:
Violet said that she had heard the cuckoo. She said it quite cheerfully. I was surprised because I thought she hated it.

Ann looks very thin. Johnie has got a cold

20th April:
Ann has started to join in the walks with Andrew and Violet. She comes back looking much less pale, and said she thought it was doing her good. Meanwhile I stay behind with Johnie.

Considering the situation, we have quite a jolly time in the evenings when they come in.

27th April:
Last night Bristles asked to go out. I opened the front door and was amazed by what I saw. On the ground was about a foot of snow and the whole scene was a deep red colour. I went up the path to the road and looked across the field between us and a neighbour's house, and there below the valley was a crashed aeroplane on fire. Flames from it were reaching up into the night sky, ammunition was exploding like fireworks. People from the village were running down Corpse Lane towards it. Only one of the crew survived, and that was the rear gunner, who was able to get out. He was carried up to the pub on two hurdles lashed together. He was badly hurt.

29th April:
I heard today from Mrs. Attwood that it was a Canadian bomber on a training flight. The sudden freak snow-storm had caused snow to settle on the wings just after take-off, which had made it crash.

The village policeman stood guard over the wrecked plane until some airmen came and took over. Two days later it was removed. It left a long black scar of burnt fuel across the field.

203

My Diary, 8th May:

Ann has been digging in the garden, ready to plant potatoes. It has been too wet before. I told her I would do it on Sunday (tomorrow), but she thought she'd have a go at it. She fainted twice - Mrs. Attwood said, "She shouldn't ought to have done it. She's not strong enough - I told her so."

Things are going well in Africa, but not in Burma. We don't discuss it.

CHAPTER 48

It was the beginning of May 1943 when the Ordinance Corps took a barn in the village and started what amounted to a cottage industry, employing the villagers on a casual basis - the pay for men was 1/6d an hour for men and 1/- per hour for women. It was known as 'The Packing Station'.

The work was packing small spares for army vehicles and tanks in waterproof paper, in readiness for amphibian landings that were to take place on the Continent at some time in the future. They had to be labelled correctly and not rattle in their boxes.

As I wouldn't be leaving home, I saw that going there would be well within my promise to Ian. I enrolled at once. It was wonderful, and I even earned a little money.

Violet had to look after Johnie and get the lunch, such as it was. The other workers were mostly old or infirm and came for only two or three hours a day. There was one other girl called Mary Davis. She had an invalid mother at home, which was the reason she had not been called up. Only she and I worked full-time, together with a Colonel of 70, who had lost a leg in the First World War - Colonel Moulton. Amongst us also were a number of rough women, who came from a gypsy place outside the next village. They fell to fighting amongst themselves from time to time. There was one very old man, who used to come occasionally. He was very thin and bent, with a purple face and red eyes.

Every week we had a visit from the Depot. Officers were driven over by ATS drivers. They came to inspect our work and encourage us to carry on the good work. They were immaculately turned out in their uniforms. The women had perfect hair, brilliant make-up and khaki stockings. The men wore gloves and carried canes, their shoes shone - they seemed to come from another planet. Sometimes one of these celestial beings would come over and ask how I was getting on. One officer with a small moustache looked curiously at me and inquired why I was there, but I was shy and embarrassed, and he turned smartly away.

My Diary, 19th May:

Two days ago we bombed two dams in Germany and breached them. It is marvellous because the water produced power for the Ruhr. Now they are empty. Violet said, "What an awful thing to do; I expect a lot of people will have been swept away and there'll be no electric light."

Andrew has gone back. It will be so dreary without him. He came to see me at the Packing Station before he went. I feel bereft. I think we all do. Johnie asked where he was. Violet told him that he had gone to do his flying again.

A plane pulling a target goes round and round, followed by another aircraft shooting at it. They keep at it all day. Johnie takes a great interest in it. He found a stick that looks like a gun and he rushed out into the garden, firing into the air. Violet took the stick away from him and threw it into the field. He cried and screamed. Violet said, "I can't think where he got the idea from. I suppose it was from pictures in the paper, or perhaps seeing the Home Guard go by."

23rd May:

My mother said it would be better not to mention anything to do with bombing or the war in front of Violet.

Ann had a letter from Ian via the Red Cross. She didn't mention it to Violet.

I'm sure Violet thinks David is dead.

Mrs. Attwood hasn't been well, so she hasn't been coming - Ann has done her best to tidy up and keep things going, but there seems a lot to do when I get home in the evening.

Vanessa wrote and told us that Uncle James had been badly injured - not on active service, but in a road accident in Egypt. "It will give me a little holiday to know that he isn't in the fighting, for a while, anyway."

We heard that my cousin 'Silly' was engaged to be married to a man in the Commandos.

I had a letter from my Smelly Friend from school. Her letter said that she was working in Bletchingly on very exciting things and felt she was really doing something worthwhile. I never answered her letter. I didn't want to tell her that I was just wrapping nuts and bolts in waterproof oiled paper. I thought about Andrew all the time and I got unbelievably depressed, chiefly about what the future held for me - I even thought vaguely about killing myself.

My Diary, Thursday, 3rd June:

Colonel Bolton has automatically assumed responsibility for the Packing Station. It's just as well - it would be chaos if he hadn't. He is ever so jolly, and when we have our tea-break, he, Mary Davis and I have a good laugh. He very kindly offered me his clothes coupons. "What does an old codger like me want with clothes," he said. Now I shall be able to buy a jersey and skirt. Making conversation at supper tonight, I told everybody about it. Violet said, "It sounds quite like a budding romance to me; you are a dark horse, Hannah." I could have hit her. I wished I'd kept my mouth shut.

CHAPTER 49

Violet said, "I should very much like to go and see my father and Aunt Jean. Do you think all of you could look after Johnie for just a couple of nights while I'm away?"

My mother was far from enthusiastic, but said, "I'm sure we could manage between us." So the date was fixed. When Violet went, Johnie cried. He didn't like being left behind, and had never been separated from his mother before.

Mrs. Attwood was better and had come back to work. She tutted when she heard that Violet had gone for a holiday.

The two days went very quickly and I don't think Johnie really noticed his mother's absence.

At the appointed time of Violet's return, I drove to Banbury Station to be there at 6.30 in the evening. I left the others at home. It was lovely and sunny. As I sat waiting, I watched all the coming and going - mostly servicemen and women. There were two American soldiers with girls. One had his girl up against a wall, and they were engaged in a passionate embrace. Another American was sitting on the station steps - he was very drunk. Every now and then he shouted something at the passers-by.

I waited and waited, but Violet never came. It went through my mind that perhaps there had been an air raid somewhere, or perhaps her father had been taken ill and she couldn't let us know. After sitting there for two hours, I left for home. When I walked into Chapel House and they saw that I was alone, everybody was alarmed.

It was decided that I should go to the Post Office and ring up Mr. Waring, but first we had to find one of his letters with the telephone number on it. There followed a frenzied search. We found one of his letters propped up behind the clock on the kitchen mantelpiece.

I went at once. Miss Turner answered the door and let me in. I asked her if I could use the telephone. The little Post Office had the cottage smell of damp and whitewash and was full of shadows, although it was still light outside, being summer and double summer time. The operator got me the number. Aunt Jean answered - the line wasn't very good. "I'll get Alfred." Mr. Waring came. "It's Hannah," I said. "I went to fetch Violet from the station and she hasn't arrived; when did she leave you?" He was rather deaf. I repeated, "Has Violet left?" "I don't understand," he said. "When did Violet leave your house?" I shouted.

"I can't hear very well - I'll fetch Jean."

Jean came back to the telephone and I asked her the same question.

"I don't know what you are talking about, Violet has not been here."

She sounded very cross, as though I were accusing her of something. I rang off.

I felt shaken. I went back home and told my mother.

At about 12 o'clock that night a car drew up outside Chapel House. It was Violet. She ran up the path and burst into the hall.

"I need some money for the taxi," she said breathlessly. "There were none at the station when I arrived, but this one drove up and I persuaded him to bring me."

After she'd paid the taxi driver and come back in, my mother said, "I need an explanation."

Violet retorted, "I don't have to explain anything to anybody. We'll talk in the morning. At the moment I'm exhausted and starving, I'm going to get myself something to eat."

My mother commented sadly, "What has got into the girl?"

In the morning my mother confronted her.

"What have you got to say about last night?"

"I haven't got anything to say," Violet replied.

"I think you have," my mother said vehemently. "We were so worried when you failed to arrive at Banbury Station, that Hannah went to the Post Office and rang your father. Don't forget we're looking after you on David's behalf."

Violet started to cry. She sat down and blew her nose.

"I went to stay with my friend Doreen in London. I decided not to go to my father after all."

"Why didn't you tell us?" my mother asked. "You only had to tell us."

"I didn't think you'd approve."

All through this discussion Ann had been a spectator. She looked from speaker to speaker, turning her head this way and that as though she was watching a tennis match. I remember thinking how ridiculous it looked.

It was a shock to find out that Violet hadn't spoken the truth. We didn't tell Mrs. Attwood about what had happened. We were afraid of what she might say. What she did say to Violet accusingly was, "So you're back then."

After my father died, my mother got the habit or going to bed or shutting herself in her room whenever things became stressful, but by this time she had more or less recovered and was able to face the difficulties that came our way, without resorting to this ploy - which made things much more bearable. She still carried Bristles about a lot. He didn't ever seem to object.

My Diary, 26th June:
The news is that the bombing of the Continent is intensifying - the Ruhr, Italy and all over the place are getting it.

Violet has not been very well. She has had a stomach upset.

My mother wanted her to go to the doctor. She said she would but then she changed her mind. She said there was no need. We thought it might have been the guinea-fowl, but none of the rest of us were affected.

A fight broke out at the Packing Station between some of the women. One woman hit another in the face and smashed her glasses. It was most exciting and alleviated the monotony no end! Colonel Moulton tried to intervene. Afterwards he said the only way to stop women fighting is to hose them down with cold water, but there was none to hand.

My mother said, "I'll never give up hope of seeing David alive."

CHAPTER 50

My Diary, 1st July:

Copied from the newspaper into my diary:

The critics of the unconditional surrender policy adopted at the Casablanca Conference were answered by Churchill today when he received the Freedom of the City of London at the Guildhall ceremony. 'To those who argue that the policy will stiffen the resistance of the enemy,' he said, 'we must take all those far-sighted measures which are necessary to prevent the world from being again convulsed, wrecked and blackened by their calculated plots and ferocious aggressions.'

Churchill believes that if a set of peace terms was drawn up, as the critics suggest, public opinion would demand conditions that would be more repulsive to the Germans than anything indicated by the general expression, 'Unconditional Surrender'. Attempts have, in fact, been made to draft a statement of conditions that could be put to Germany. Churchill says that they looked so terrible when written down, that they were scrapped at once. He believes the Allies must completely break the Nazi, Fascist and Japanese tyrannies, but without being moved by mere lust for vengeance.

5th July:

General Sikorski has been killed in an air crash in Gibraltar. They say it wasn't sabotage - I expect it was.

Ann has been working in the garden. Thanks to her efforts, we have been having lovely new potatoes. They were put in rather late because of the weather. Her health has improved enormously with working in the garden and being out of doors in all weathers. - Now we are worried about Violet.

11th July:

Yesterday we made a landing in Sicily. A great storm blew up in the Mediterranean and threatened the success of the whole operation, but suddenly the wind abated and the sea calmed. Although delayed, the invasion was able to go ahead. By dawn there were 150,000 British and American troops ashore and more on their way. It is terribly exciting.

We had a visit from the Depot. Our work has been so satisfactory that we are going to be promoted from packing nuts and bolts to small electrical parts.

20th July:
Although the capturing of almost all of Sicily has been so quick and successful, it seems as though the war will go on for ever and ever.

We had a visit from Misses Bates - they brought us some gooseberries. Now that the Reichs have left for America they seem quite lost.

We wandered out into the garden with them, and Miss Mary moaned as she looked round. "I remember this when it was full of flowers; it's a good thing that poor Pamela can't see it now," she said. "I suppose you've dug up most of her plants and thrown them away. I wish you'd given us the chance of saving some of them."

Ann was quite annoyed.

Violet took Johnie to the doctor because of a spot on his leg.

CHAPTER 51

My Diary, 31st July:

Violet had a letter telling her that David has been reported a prisoner in Japanese hands. It was so wonderful, we couldn't believe it. Violet was overcome.

I remember it so clearly. Almost as though it were happening now. When Violet opened the letter, she said she thought she was going to faint, so she ran into the garden. I ran after her to ask what the matter was.

"It's wonderful news," she said faintly, and sat down on the ground, starting to cry.

She handed me the letter and I ran to tell my mother.

The letter said:

'We are glad to learn that Capt. David Brocus has been reported to be a Prisoner of War in Japanese hands, after so many months of anxious waiting for news.

IMPORTANT

Your attention is drawn to the fact that, if possible, all letters to him should be written in BLOCK CAPITALS or TYPED. Send your letter for your Prisoner of War to the above address. Please be sure to write his rank, initials, personal number, name and address, and also your own, clearly. In the interests of all Prisoners of War in the Far East, families are asked to send no more than one letter to each man once a fortnight. If too many letters are sent, there will be delays in censorship.

You will always receive any official information concerning your Prisoner of War direct, and we are not able to make enquiries of this nature.

If you have any problems or difficulties, please do not hesitate to write to us.'

You can imagine how we felt. We were aghast with relief and, at the same time, horrified by what might be happening to him so far away. I secretly wondered how prisoners of the Japanese would ever be found, so that they could be freed alive. Even Mrs. Attwood was overcome by the news.

It was a beautiful summer day and a Sunday. We were still basking in the joy of hearing that David was alive. Violet had been to early service, and after breakfast she and I got a picnic together of sorts and at lunchtime took it down to the stream below the house. Because of the dry weather there wasn't much water, only the slightest trickle, enough though for Johnie to get soaked and muddy in no time at all. Sylvia Havers came with Theresa. We sat on the grass under the oak trees, watching the children playing in the dappled sunlight - Bristles came meowing down the hill.

I thought Violet looked very pale beside Ann, who had got very brown working in the garden. Her legs were brown too. I started to think about Marchfold and all the wild flowers that grew there in the fields and along the banks of the streams. "This is a bleak place," my mother said. "Higher and colder than Sussex and less hospitable."

My mother was wearing her straw hat. There was a hole in the brim. Jagged bits of straw showed where the break was. She sat there rhythmically waving a hand to and fro to keep the flies off her sandwich. She made me think of Granny Bell.

Sylvia sat smiling plumply - her face was as smooth and trouble-free as a newly blown up balloon. Nothing seemed to worry her.

"Poor Father," she said, "Sunday is a rotten day for him. He has to take one service after another and rush between the churches."

I could see that Violet was shocked.

"Surely," she whispered, "it is his whole mission in life to sustain and uphold the ministry?"

Sylvia shrugged her shoulders.

Theresa started to cry because Johnie had splashed her.

* * * * *

I woke up in the middle of the night and saw that there was light under my door. I looked at my watch - it was just after 1 o'clock. The light was on in the hall. I went down and opened the kitchen door. Sitting at the kitchen table was Violet; in front of her was a blank sheet of paper. She looked up at me and exclaimed "Hannah!" She had been crying: "I'm trying to write to David," she said, pushing back her hair from her tear-sodden face. Her hands were trembling.

I made her a milk drink.

"Go to bed now," I suggested. "Tomorrow you'll be more able to cope."

I pointed out to her that the blackout curtains hadn't been properly drawn together. "We'd better not get slack about it," I said, "or we may be sorry. Remember the uncovered sky-light down the road and what happened there with the whistling bomb."

Next day she sent her letter off.

My Diary, August 1943:

Ripening corn stretches into the distance across the countryside. Because of the blockade at sea, permanent pasture has been ploughed up and sown to keep us in bread and the farm beasts alive. There hasn't been so much cultivation since the previous panic - the shortage of grain in the Napoleonic Wars.

The sky was full of larks.

Saturday, 14th August:

Andrew is at the Vicarage on leave. He has been posted abroad. We guess to the Middle East.

We all seem very flat and discouraged.

He has only been over twice and there are only five days left of his time.

20th August:

Andrew has gone.

He didn't come and say goodbye.

From the Regiment, 3rd September 1943:

'Dear Mrs Brocus,
Communications with the Far East
In accordance with the new instructions, only twenty-five words may now be sent to Prisoners of War in the Far East.

We are therefore reducing your letter to a brief message, and we are returning the first one herewith for your approval and posting. (No stamp is required.) '

Another letter came for Violet dated 6/9/43. It was from the Red Cross, Prisoners of War Department:

'Dear Mrs. Brocus,
We have been officially advised that your husband is a prisoner of war in Japanese hands. We are glad that this news of his safety has at last been received.

Arrangements have been made for the transmission of letters to prisoners of war in the Far East, and the enclosed leaflet will give you full details.

The present position in regard to parcels is given on the back of this letter.

We should like you to know that we shall retain complete records at this office of your husband, and shall be only too pleased to render you every assistance at any time, should you either call or write to us. If you write, would you kindly quote the above reference, as this will enable us to give you prompt attention.

Parcels
Parcels cannot be sent at present, owing to the refusal of the Japanese to grant safe conduct for ships that would have to be utilised for such a parcels service. Every endeavour is being made to secure a change in their present attitude and, if as a result of these efforts facilities are accorded, the next of kin will be advised. Full details will also be published in the press.

The organisation, in collaboration with other national Red Cross Societies, is meanwhile doing everything possible to help Far East prisoners by providing food, medicines, clothing and other supplies. Already several thousand tons of such supplies have been shipped to the Far East, and distributed equally amongst all prisoners of allied nationality in Japanese hands. Plans have been made, and continue to be made, for the supplementing of these supplies by further despatches, and by local purchases in the Far East.

CHAPTER 52

My Diary, Friday, 10th September:

We have landed on the toe of Italy at Salerno and other places. The Italians have surrendered, but the Germans are rushing to fill the gaps they have left.

Ann has gone home to her mother.

Over the wireless, the Germans are saying that they have dreadful secret weapons in store for us. I am afraid.

We continually bomb Penenunder on the Baltic. There must be something sinister there, and something else horrible inland on the French coast.

30th September:

Australian Special Group have got into Singapore Harbour and blown up a lot of ships. I hardly dare think about it, but we are slowly gaining ground everywhere.

Copied from a newspaper:

'Britain's war effort is being hampered by a wave of unofficial strikes, nine thousand engineers are out at Vickers Armstrong at Barrow-in-Furness. They have been on strike for two weeks in protest at the arbitration award on rates of pay. Striking is illegal under an Order of 1940, but the impracticality of sending strikers to prison was demonstrated last year at Betteshanger Colliery in Kent. More than 1,000 summonses were taken out against strikers. They were fired, while their Union Branch officials were sent to prison for a month. When miners refused to pay, magistrates could not have them arrested because there was not enough room in the prisons.

The same difficulty now applies to a strike of 7,000 miners in the Lanarkshire Coalfield in Scotland. This year has already seen a dock strike at Liverpool, and now a strike of 16,000 workers at the Rolls-Royce aero-engine factory at Hillington. Glasgow is threatened over unequal rates of pay for women, who now make up two-thirds of the workforce.

How is this possible, while men are dying to preserve their right to strike?

2nd October:
We have taken Naples. It is really autumn now - misty and cold - I lit the fire this evening.

Chapter 53

One evening, we were sitting after supper when I looked at Violet and I suddenly saw that she had changed. I couldn't exactly put my finger on what it was. I wondered how David would feel when he came back, finding her altered. I looked at her again and decided that she had just got fatter. After all, our food was fairly stodgy. I also noticed that she had some grey hairs, which shocked me.

My mother said, "Yes, she has put on weight. Don't worry about the grey hairs, lots of people have white hairs in their early twenties. She probably won't get many more for years." I expect it was because of having Johnie.

Our relationship with the Havers was not bad at this time. I went over every week to borrow books and, although I never failed to take them back the following week before taking more, Mr. Havers always said, "Be sure to take care of them, and bring them back safely - I don't really like lending books anyway."

Sylvia and Violet were constant companions, although they had left off going to Banbury shopping together. Johnie and Theresa played nearly every day.

My mother had withdrawn somewhat from Mrs. Havers' company. I think it was because she had discovered her to be more boring than she had expected. Nevertheless, we helped each other along and shared our family news, both good and bad.

My Diary, Wednesday, 13th October:
The Italians have declared war on the Germans. The free French have taken Corsica.

It'll soon be my birthday again. My mother mentioned it. When she had gone out of the room, Violet said to me, "Hannah, you should get out into the world. If you don't, you'll suddenly find that life has passed you by and it's too late."

It was Sunday, 28th October. Violet went to early service as she always did. When she came back, she went straight upstairs. I could hear her crying. I tried to find out what was wrong, but she seemed unable to speak. My mother came up. We tried to calm her. Between gasps she said, "Mr. Havers refused to give me communion - he passed me by."

My mother repeated, "Refused to give you communion - why? On what grounds and by what authority could he possibly do that? I shall go to the Vicarage at once and confront him. Don't be upset Violet, it's some silly mistake or understanding." She went and got her hat and coat and put it on as though it were armour. I went with her. I had to take Johnie because I didn't feel he could be left behind with Violet.

When we rang the bell at the Vicarage, the door was quickly opened by the Vicar himself. He stepped back on seeing us. My mother walked straight into the hall. We followed her.

"By what authority and for what reason did you dare to withhold communion from my daughter-in-law? I want to know," she demanded.

Mr. Havers' face went very red.

"I would choose not to have to tell you myself," he replied, "but since you ask me, I will. I refused her communion because of my deep conviction of the sanctity of marriage and of the marriage vows. It may seem strange to you, but I happen to have a deep sense of the Biblical laws of right and wrong. Here you come to my house, creating uproar on a Sunday, when I am extremely busy, to take me to task and question my judgement. I am only just now able to snatch a little breakfast. I must ask you to leave my house at once and not interrupt the day further. I have work to do."

Mrs. Havers, hearing the commotion, had come into the hall. She stood there hovering, pale and trembling.

"How dare you call Violet an adulteress!" my mother shouted.

The Vicar intoned the words, "because she is."

"I shall write to the Bishop. I think the whole thing is absolutely shocking."

"So it is," the Vicar agreed vehemently.

With that, my mother turned to go and we stormed out, leaving the door open. It closed behind us.

As we walked away, I suddenly had a feeling that I was going to laugh.

Johnie asked, "Why was he so cross?"

When we got home, we went upstairs to Violet's room. She was lying on the bed, looking at the ceiling.

My mother told her what had happened and what had been said at the Vicarage.

She sat up, looked straight at my mother, and said, "I am going to have a baby."

My mother's face went from red to white. I was frightened.

"I suppose Andrew is the father."

Violet didn't answer, but nodded.

"Does he know?" my mother asked.

"No. I didn't want to make things worse for him. They are bad enough as they are. You see, I thought David was dead."

Nobody talked in our house for days. There was a great silence, only relieved by the sound of Johnie playing happily with his cars.

Violet stayed upstairs. I took her food and drink.

At the end of that dreadful time, late one night, Violet came down to get herself something to eat. My mother walked into the kitchen to find her there eating some cold potatoes. She went up to her and putting her arms round her, drew her into a close embrace. Violet put her head on my mother's shoulder and cried as though she would never stop, but presently she calmed down and they both sat by the fire.

"What am I going to do?" Violet said. "What will David say when he comes home? With Andrew, it was as though David had come back to me. It just happened. We were both unhappy, and I loved Andrew as though he were David."

"We must tell them at the Vicarage," my mother said, but Violet pleaded with her not to. "It'll only make things worse for him and he's away flying. Anyway, what could he do if he were here? If he knew?"

We didn't see Sylvia for two weeks. Then one evening she

crept in. She looked very upset. I had no idea that she could look like that. She knew Violet was pregnant. She also knew that it was Andrew's baby.

"I want you to tell them at the Vicarage - you must," she told Violet. "They're sure to find out sooner or later anyway. If you don't tell them, someone else will. They must know that it's my brother. If you don't then I shall."

In the end, Violet's argument prevailed.

I asked Sylvia to take back the last book that I had borrowed from her father. I remember that it was Arabia Deserter. I wasn't enjoying it much anyway. It was a very boring book.

CHAPTER 54

It was at about this time that the anonymous letters started coming. I think they were probably written by one or two people, but they came regularly for a while and then stopped, only to start again later on.

Violet's brother Stephen came home from Ireland, a short while afterwards. He had embarkation leave and came to see Violet before he sailed.

Being in the Army had changed him from a rather weedy youth into a strapping young man with a brown face. He was hardly recognisable. He came to spend the night.

"I am sorry to see Violet so worn-looking," he said to my mother. "It must be a terrible worry for her to have David in a Japanese prisoner of war camp, although at least she now knows that he is alive."

Violet asked me (when there was an opportunity) to tell Stephen what had happened. "We've always been so fond of each other, I feel he must 'know'," she said. After supper, when he and I were alone, I told him.

He was very shocked.

"I can't believe it," he said. "She couldn't do a thing like that to David. What a dreadful thing to happen. I don't know what to say."

He sat silent, but after a while he said.

"I don't think I'll stay if you don't mind - I think I'll push off."

Although it was past ten and a rough night, he gathered his things together and walked out. He left without saying goodbye either to Violet or my mother. I tried to persuade him to stay till morning, but he was too upset even to speak.

Mrs. Attwood wrote a letter to my mother. In it she said that she was feeling her age and felt it was time to stop going out to work. 'It is sad to say, Madam,' the letter ended, 'but things are not as good as they might be at Chapel House.'

My mother asked Violet if Andrew wrote to her. She didn't

say anything for a long time, but my mother persisted.

"Does he?"

Violet answered, "No."

"Or, are you writing to him?"

"No, I'm not," Violet said, her voice rising, and she started to cry.

"Because if you are, you are continuing to be unfaithful to David and I think perhaps it would be better if you went to live with your father."

But, of course, my mother couldn't ever have turned her out. She still belonged to David and then there was Johnie, and we felt responsible for them both. We loved Johnie passionately and he belonged to us. The thought of him going away would have been unbearable.

I see I didn't write in my diary for some weeks, but there is an entry on 27th November:

Ann has come back. She seems very impatient with Violet and speaks to her in a very dismissive tone of voice. I wish she wouldn't. I am so sorry for Violet. Ann asked me what was extra wrong with Violet. I told her. She didn't know anything about it - I thought she did. She said, "How sad for everybody."

The baby is due in early March, or so it is thought. Dr. Brand has been very kind to her. Ann has got herself a full-time job at the Airmen's Convalescent Home at Bisham House, as secretary to the Commandant. She has bought herself a bicycle to get to and fro. The only thing is that is downhill going and uphill all the way home, but it is conveniently near. It was at Bisham House that they got a whistling bomb in the garden after showing a light through a sky-light. Lucky it didn't hit the house.

1st December:
I'm afraid Violet is getting letters from Andrew AND writing to him, although she said she wasn't.

The Misses Bates came. They were in church when Violet was refused communion. They were shocked. Miss Frances asked my mother whatever was the reason the Vicar gave for doing such a thing. My mother told her.

"He still had no right whatsoever to take such a step on his own judgement." Miss Frances paused. "This is a very sad thing to have happened and very hard for you to have Violet living under your roof, knowing that she has betrayed your son. She spent a lot of time in the summer with that Havers' boy. I did wonder at the time if it was wise. I don't expect the Vicar has thought of that yet."

My mother remained silent.

My Diary, 14th December:
It is hard to realise that I am now 21. Nobody has noticed.

My mother doesn't know whether to tell the Aunts about Violet, or not, or which Aunts to tell. She sat down to write to Aunt May, but she couldn't think what to say, so she put it off. They've got to know sometime.

Violet doesn't go out at all now - only into the garden and she comes in when our neighbour looks over the fence. He doesn't do it much because it is wintertime and cold.

Nurse Wickens comes to see Violet. She isn't very nice to her.

My mother is thinking about us all going back to London - that is, if she can get the bombed-out furniture moved.

The Germans are threatening secret weapons.

18th December:
Sylvia came round rather late in the evening to see Violet. They went up to Violet's bedroom and talked. It was past eleven before she left.

Christmas is looming up. We mustn't deprive Johnie of fun, even though none of us feels like even thinking about it. Sylvia will not be able to bring Theresa to play, it wouldn't be allowed. I don't believe the Havers know that Sylvia comes to see us.

It is very cold at the Packing Station. I stuff straw that comes with the boxes up my trousers to keep warm. There is no heating.

We were registered at the village shop for our rations, so I had to go there every week. It was something of an ordeal because of the sullen and accusing looks that I got from the other customers. For that reason, I tried to go when there were few people about. Luckily, Mrs. Green had remained fairly friendly and kept scarce things under the counter for me. Every time I went she plied me with questions as to how we were getting on, and the state of Violet's health. She always asked after my mother, and nearly always ended our conversation with the remark, "I don't know how she carries on - if it were me, I don't think I could."

CHAPTER 55

It was the New Year 1944.

Early in January, Violet had a postcard. This was it:

IMPERIAL JAPANESE ARMY

I AM INTERNED IN: No 6 P.O.W. THAILAND CAMP

MY HEALTH IS   EXCELLENT
I AM ILL IN HOSPITAL

I AM WORKING   FOR PAY
NOT WORKING

PLEASE SEE THAT   EVERYONE IS TAKEN CARE OF

MY LOVE TO YOU
David Brocus

David had crossed out 'I AM ILL IN HOSPITAL' and 'I AM NOT WORKING'. It was all printed except David's writing in the words 'Everyone' and his name.

At least we knew that he was still alive.

Violet looked more unhappy than anyone had ever seen. She also was very pregnant by that time.

My Diary, 15th January:

My mother and I went to London to look at the house and see if we could arrange for the stuff to be moved out of it. It was a very depressing day. We had to queue for ages for a taxi at Paddington. Everywhere looked so dingy, and we were sent from one office to another. At last one man said he would do his best, and would let us know when and if the house was cleared.

Looking at No. 12 in its present state of damage and dirt, having it emptied would only be the beginning of our difficulties, and my mother wondered how it would suit Johnie to be in London anyway.

We were exhausted and thankful when we got back to Chapel House. Johnie came running to the front door. Ann had got supper for everyone.

Violet was cheered up a little by the idea of going back to London.

My Diary, 1st February:

London has been bombed again. They say it is retaliation for our bombing of Berlin. The Germans claimed that 600 bombers took part.

Wouldn't this happen, just when we were thinking of going back.

We have made another landing on the leg of Italy at Anzio to relieve the fierceness of the fighting further south at Casino. It doesn't seem to be going well. I think the war will go on for ever. Anyway, for years and years. Sometimes the Allies are winning, sometimes the others. I said this to my mother. She said, "You're wrong! We are slowly pushing forward all the time!" I hope she believes it.

There have been official statements about the cruel things the Japanese are doing to the Prisoners of War. That the prisoners live in inhuman conditions and are tortured. I don't think my mother heard it - thank goodness.

It's really getting close to the time for Violet's baby to be born.

Saturday, 20th February:

The most awful thing has happened - Sylvia's husband has been killed in Italy. She has left the Vicarage and gone up north to stay with her in-laws, taking Theresa with her. She came and told us. She looked terrible - not like herself at all.

Violet is crying all the time. I told her it wasn't good for the baby, but she went on just the same.

"Are you crying for David or Andrew?" I asked her. She said, "both," and then she blurted out that Andrew had stopped writing to her. She seemed to have forgotten that she told my mother that he didn't write to her anymore. I thought she wasn't speaking the truth at the time, but I had never seen a letter for her with a Forces post office stamp on it, so I came to the conclusion that I had been wrong in suspecting her. "I haven't had a letter from him in two months now," she said. "I expect he's trying to forget about me."

I played with Johnie in the snow, but there wasn't enough to do anything with.

24th February:

Dr. Brand came to see my mother. He told her that we should try not to leave Violet alone too much - especially with Johnie. My mother asked him to have a word with Nurse Wickens, and ask her if she could be kinder to Violet. He is going to arrange for the baby to be born in Banbury Hospital - it's a good idea in the circumstances. I'm thankful because it could be quite frightening if the baby started to come and neither Nurse Wickens or Dr. Brand were here. I haven't the faintest idea what to do. As it is, I've got to get her to hospital and that's worrying enough. I must remember to save enough petrol for the car.

There have been aeroplanes flying round and round, pulling gliders. I wonder what they are going to be used for. They look so flimsy.

I'm always glad when I hear Ann arriving back from the Convalescent Home. Some evenings she is very restless and goes to bed very early.

CHAPTER 56

I remember looking at Violet and at her huge bulge. However the baby was going to manage to get out amazed me. I wondered about Andrew and Violet together, and tried not to think about their secret times. In a way I was glad that Violet had comforted him when his hands were burnt and he was so wretched and shocked. I only wished, with a great longing, that it had been me, and then remembered what she had done to David and felt disloyal and guilty.

I asked Violet if she had thought about getting her things ready for her stay in hospital. She said she hadn't. We tried to look out Johnie's old baby things. We searched through all the boxes in the hall, but didn't find them. Violet said, "there'll be plenty of time after it's born."

It was 18th March. Fortunately, a Saturday so I was at home. Violet said she had a pain. I ran round to Dr. Brand and told him I was far from calm. He followed me back to Chapel House and had a look at Violet. He thought she should go without delay. He asked me if I could manage, and I said I could. He helped me get Violet into the car. My mother stayed behind with Johnie. It wasn't quite dark, which helped driving with the dimmed, covered headlamps.

Banbury Hospital was always spoken of by the village in tones of ultimate dread. Certainly, when we arrived in front of the gaunt grey building, I felt I was taking Violet to the Workhouse. Inside the passages were dimly lit, probably because of the blackout. There was an overpowering smell of disinfectant, the walls echoed with the clatter of bedpans, the clamour of voices and the clanking of trolleys.

I looked at Violet - her face was taut with anxiety. I put my arm round her. "You'll soon be home," I said, "don't worry." It was then that a grey-haired nurse appeared from another world. She was starched and stiff as a dummy-board, but radiant with kindness. She gently took Violet into her care and led her away.

On the way home, I cried.

From what Ann had said to me, I realised how depressed she

had become. The event of Violet's baby had stirred up all the memories of her miscarriage and reminded her of the disappointment and unhappiness she had suffered. It also brought into focus the misery of Ian being a prisoner of war, and the prospect of years without him, with only hope of his return - not certainty.

The next day my mother and I went to the hospital at visiting time - 5.30 to 8 o'clock.

"Can we leave Johnie with you?" my mother asked Ann.

"I suppose so," she replied, "if you must."

At the hospital, we found our way to Violet. She was lying with her eyes shut - the baby was brought. It was a girl. The most beautiful baby. Not red and wrinkled at all, but very pretty and plump.

My mother asked what it was going to be called. Violet didn't answer at first, then she said, "You suggest a name."

Neither of us could think of anything to say after that, so we sat by her bed in silence. Not that it was silence. There was a great noise of chattering and babies crying and of food being brought round.

"Why don't you call her after your mother?" my mother suggested.

"That's an idea," Violet said, "but I don't think I will somehow."

We stayed for an hour. On the way out, the grey-haired nurse waylaid us. "Are you Mrs. Brocus's family?" she asked. "I'm very worried about her, she's so unhappy. I've told her she must look forward to the time when her husband gets back, and to think how delighted he'll be when he finds that he's got a beautiful little daughter."

We didn't go to the hospital to visit again, because of the petrol, but fetched Violet home within the week.

"I would really have liked to stay in hospital forever," she said, "and not come back."

My mother promised her that Nurse Wickins would be kept away.

Johnie was thrilled with the baby at first.

My Diary, 23rd March:

236

A glider came down in the field where the other aeroplane crashed. In almost exactly the same spot. By the time I had a chance to go down and look at it, a policeman was already there guarding it. I don't think anyone was hurt. It looked like a broken bird, flat on the ground. By evening it had been taken away.

I am quite tired - I was up several times in the night. Once with the baby, and once with Johnie, who had had a nightmare. I suppose we shall get through all this. It has been decided to call the baby Daisy.

Dr. Brand came to see Violet. He says that she should rest in bed as much as possible for the time being.

Ann had a puncture in the front tyre of her bicycle. I had to drive her to Bisham House, which made me late for work.

The Chivdit Commander Wingate has been killed in an air crash. Opinion is very divided about him. It hardly bears thinking about, but the Japanese are nearing the Indian border. What will happen if they take India? I suppose the Chivdits hope to cut them off behind.

27th March:

My mother and I went into Banbury to register the baby. The name of the father was put down as David Brocus, Army Officer.

That is the end of our petrol till next month. No more left.

30th March:

For the past twenty-four hours, all the roads in the village and surrounding lanes have been blocked by tanks and armoured cars. They are all Canadians. Everywhere you look, there are tanks, as far as you can see.

Poor Ann had to push her bicycle all the way to Bisham through them. She was taking it to the handyman to mend down there, and she had to walk back. She felt terribly conspicuous. They were whistling and calling after her all the way. It was quite encouraging, she said, in a way, and quite funny. I had

237

the same thing happen when going to the Packing Station, but it was only a little way for me. I wished the earth would open and swallow me. I could hardly walk, and my legs became sort of paralysed with self-consciousness.

There was a terrible fuss because Johnie put Bristles into the pram on top of the baby.

I lie in bed at night, listening to the bombers flying out and I hear them return at dawn. There are stragglers, limping back in ones and twos. I try not to think about what may have happened to them.

CHAPTER 57

I came home to lunch and, to my great surprise, found Aunt May sitting at the table eating. I was a bit taken aback because I knew my mother hadn't told any of the family about the baby.

When I entered the room, I didn't know what the state of play was. It seemed that Aunt May had written to tell us that Uncle Donald was going up to Scotland for a few days, and she intended to take the opportunity to come and see us.

"You've still got the same dreadful old cat," she remarked. "Isn't it time you got a new one?"

My mother replied in an offended tone of voice, "I'd have you know that Bristles understands every word you say. He's not a dreadful cat at all, he's one of the family."

"Funny sort of family," May said.

It was then that the baby started to cry upstairs.

My mother said, "That's Daisy crying upstairs. Violet's looking after her at the moment. I'll tell you about it later."

Johnie pulled his spoon out of his mouth and said, through a mouthful of potato, "I'm very lutty to have a baby sister of my own, but I would have much more liker to have a bruver."

That evening we told Aunt May what had happened.

She asked my mother how furious she was with Violet, adding, "it would be difficult indeed to be anything but sorry for anyone who looks as unhappy as poor Violet. However, I do have to say, if she was Harry's wife, I'd kill her. Having said that, my advice to you is not to tell the rest of the family - anyway, not at present, and don't tell anyone who doesn't already know. When you leave this village and Daisy has grown up a bit, all this will be in the past. How old she is won't be counted up as it is now. David, of course, is another matter - you'll have to cope with that when the time comes, but, she is the loveliest baby."

We saw very few people from outside in those days, so it was very nice to have Aunt May to stay with us. It made a nice change.

On one day during her visit, Johnie lost his head with excitement and started 'showing off'. He pulled faces and threw himself about the room. He had never done it before and, as far as I know, never did it again. When I spoke to him afterwards, he asked, "What is showing off?" He put his arms round me, hid his face in my neck, and said, "Hannah, I wanted to be funny for Aunt May."

CHAPTER 58

It was while Aunt May was staying with us, that there was the most awful row. You could say 'quarrel', but the word 'row' is more appropriate.

It started with a discussion about the raids on Berlin. It had been given out that the casualties among bomber crews were unacceptably high. It wasn't until much later that we learnt that their chances of survival were only 50-50.

Aunt May complained furiously about the bishops and their protests about the bombings of enemy cities.

"I suppose they have no reason to want the war to come to a speedy end," she said. "They haven't got anyone belonging to them in the fighting or shut up in prison camps, and don't care to think about slave labour or the slaughter of the Jews."

Violet spoke, "I would have thought anyone would agree that what we are doing is wrong: 'Thou Shalt Not Kill', and that is the beginning and end of it."

My mother said, "You seem to have forgotten, Violet, that your husband chose to be a soldier."

Ann was exasperated. "I have heard you praise the Russians for their courage and determination in repelling the Germans."

"Of course," Violet answered, "that's entirely different - their country had been invaded. It is permissible to defend yourself if attacked, but after what we've done, do you wonder the Germans are aggressive? We've only got ourselves ... "

May interrupted her: "Do you realise that those men go out in bombers night after night, facing terrifying risks and death to protect you and make it possible for you to sit there and spout this 'righteous' piffle?"

Ann joined in, "It's no use talking to her, she's just stupid and that's her whole trouble. She can't even put together a reasonable argument - she can't even manage her own life. I don't expect she's even heard of the words 'strategy' or 'attrition'." (I hadn't heard of the word 'attrition'.) "I expect she's in no hurry to get

David home."

A lot of things were said that couldn't be unsaid. Stupid things - it was hateful.

Suddenly, Violet started to scream out, "I can't stand anymore; I can't stand anymore; I can't bear it; I can't bear it."

Johnie sat watching. I took him out of the room. His eyes were huge and dark and horrified. Looking into them, I felt as though I were looking into his skull or deep into his soul. I was afraid. It took him some time to come out of it. I could hear Violet upstairs, and the baby crying. I don't really want to remember any of it.

After Aunt May went home, we had to start living together again.

Ann tried to apologise to Violet, whose response was, "What does it matter anyway?"

My Diary, 31st March:
Got the early potatoes in.
Terrific RAF losses on a raid in Nuremburg.
Rear-gunner practice - cartridges rained down on the flat roof.
Violet a little better.

8th April:
Violet isn't very nice to Daisy.
The Japanese invasion of India has been stopped at a place called Imphal - please God don't let them get any further.

It wasn't until May that Monte Cassino was at last captured; then the road to Rome lay open at last. I thought about Sylvia's husband being killed at Anzio now that all that was over and passed by.

I continued to be worried about Violet's attitude to the baby. I once saw her throw Daisy into her cot, or rather dump her violently. I wondered whether I should speak to Dr. Brand about it, or mention it to my mother. It was at night that I felt particularly nervous. In the end, I suggested to Violet that I should have the baby to sleep with me so that she would not be disturbed. She replied, "If you want her, you have her. I don't mind."

So Daisy came into my room. I loved her being there, making small alive noises during the night. Sometimes I just stood and looked down on her in her cot. It was hard to believe that she was half Andrew's and that he didn't even know that he was the father of such a beautiful daughter. Often in the middle of the night, Johnie used to come and get into my bed.

My Diary, 12th May:

Everyone in the village was asked to pick dandelion flowers and take them to the Misses Bates on the 8th, so Johnie and I picked all day on the Sunday. A lot of people did as they were asked, and there was a huge amount of flowers gathered. It turned out that was to make some medicine or other. I have no idea what.

5th June:

We have landed on the Continent - D Day! We listen to the wireless all the time to see what is happening. Pray to God that we shall succeed. Gliders are used by the paras.

We were impotent spectators, watching the whole world raging in combat. I continued at the Packing Station. It was radio spares that I then counted interminably and put into little cardboard boxes.

The summer is with us again. The landings on the French coast prevailed.

With double summertime, the clear days seem to stretch on until midnight.

Every year I bought two packets of night-scented stock from Miss Turner at the Post Office. I took them from her seed rack and planted them by the steps outside the French windows of our big room. We used to sit there in the evenings and breath in the night air and the scent of the flowers. When the moon was full, clouds of dusky-grey moths gathered and flitted round them.

In such beautiful tranquillity, conversation was unnecessary, which was just as well, because none of us had anything left to say.

CHAPTER 59

My Diary, 13th June:
We are not making much headway in Normandy. There is considerable resistance from the Germans - I hope it is going well. The Germans are being battered by the Russians on their other side, and that's a heartening thought.

17th June:
One of Hitler's dreaded secret weapons has arrived - it is a small pilotless aeroplane. When the engine cuts out, it dives to earth and explodes. About seventy-three have landed in London so far and in the South East and there have been a lot of casualties.

23rd June:
The Japanese have been beaten at Imphal. That is indeed wonderful, wonderful news. The Chivdits keep on slogging it out at the rear in Burma, and they are winning.

Violet had seemed very off-hand with me. I wondered if I had offended her. I tried not to notice.

We were sitting in the kitchen after supper, preparing to clear away and move into the garden, when Violet stood up and said, "Hannah, I suppose you don't think I know what is going on. You are plotting to take my children away from me. First of all you snatch the baby and now you are enticing Johnie."

My Diary, 23rd July:
There has been an attempt on Hitler's life. How encouraging! Alas, it failed, although he was injured.
We were asked whether we would have another evacuee child - people are leaving London all over again because of the flying bombs, but they are being shot down at sea, or their wings tipped over so they crash. Fewer are reaching London.

We are advancing in Normandy.

Wed., 9th August:
The German officers who attempted to kill Hitler have been hanged with piano wire. A slow death filmed for the Führer's private viewing. Piano wire sounds so ghastly. Why piano wire?

Brussels has been liberated.

I love the bats flitting about the garden in the evenings.

The Colonel at the Packing Station is not well - I have taken over his duties for the time being.

Sunday, 20th August:
In Warsaw, the Poles have risen up against the Germans - expecting the advancing Russians to come to their aid and relieve them. Instead, the Russians remain at a distance, watching the city burn, waiting for the uprising to be crushed before moving forward. The Pope has pleaded with the Russians to rescue them, but to no avail. Personally, I can't see what the Pope has got to do with it or why anyone should listen to him particularly.

We asked Violet if she would like to go to church somewhere away from the village. I would drive her in the car as long as we'd got petrol. It couldn't be every Sunday, but possibly twice a month. She said how kind it was of me, but she felt it was all too difficult. "When the war is over," she said, "I'll start going to church again."

26th August:
Paris has been liberated. On the wireless I heard a reporter speaking from Notre Dame - General de Gaulle was walking down the aisle undaunted by the crackling of rifle fire still going on on the roof. I could hear it.

My mother had a letter saying that the stored furniture at No. 12 would be removed during the next two months and the property free for her to move back into again. But now, with all the flying bombs and doodle-bugs, the whole thing has changed again.

We don't want Johnie to be in London; also I have to go on working at the Packing Station, particularly now that the Colonel is away ill - perhaps forever.

29th August:
I was walking home from the village shop when I saw Mr. Havers coming towards me. The situation was inevitable - there was no escape. We passed each other with our heads turned in opposite directions - it was ridiculous.

My mother said how glad she was that we have so little contact with other people, because she can't bear anyone enquiring after David, asking her if she has heard anything of him lately. A woman collecting for the Red Cross at the door said, "At least you know he isn't cold. I understand it's always warm out there."

On the other hand, she is always furious with the family if they don't write asking about the boys, or asking about David and not Ian, or about Ian and not David.

1st September:
There has been a nationwide appeal for people to pick rosehips. The children are not getting enough fruit because none is imported. The rosehips are to be made into Vitamin C syrup. Johnie and I went picking - they were too prickly for him and I was torn to shreds.

7th September:
The blackout has been relaxed, instead it is called 'a dim out'. Normal curtaining is now allowed and there is going to be more street lighting. It doesn't really affect us here, but it will if we go to London. Defused car lights are allowed.

10th September:
There is awful talk about lack of fuel in France for the

Forces. It is said that this could lengthen the war.

17th September:
From early morning, towed gliders have been going over. The sky has been full of them, flying east.

We now know there has been an airborne drop into Holland in advance of the main attack to the south, rather like Anzio in Italy. The objective is to take two bridges on the Rhine in a place called Arnheim. It is said that this could shorten the war by months.

The garden is shockingly weedy and the pigeons have had the peas, or someone has.

There are rumours that another awful weapon is being used against us, although nothing has been said officially. But I've heard that one landed near someone who knew someone and that it made a vast hole and there was liquid red stuff all over the place.

As we advance into France, the launching sites of the V.1s have been captured: the Germans are sending them from somewhere else.

20th September:
It doesn't seem to be going very well at Arnheim. The Poles are fighting with us there. We are surrounded and cut off and no help is arriving from the main force.

27th September:
The troops in Arnheim have been forced to surrender - only a few have escaped, mostly by swimming the Rhine, or in boats. A lot have been taken prisoner, a lot killed - this is a bad day - what is going to happen to us next?

There have been personal accounts of sole survivors on the wireless. The fighting was furious both night and day without respite, and the town smashed; no water, no nothing. No relief arrived.

I find I wrote in my diary almost every day at this time, but the entries are of very little interest - mostly about the dreariness of our situation. Our household seemed to have congealed into a lump of discontent and boredom.

Everywhere though, there was a feeling of frantic urgency to beat the Germans quickly. There seemed to be an almost tangible threat hanging over us, possibly even greater than when we were expecting invasion. Although we didn't know it at the time, it was a race against time to get the atomic bomb before they did - the V.1s and V.2s were ominous signs of danger; we learnt later that they had been designed originally to carry nuclear warheads, not just high explosives.

In the Far East the Americans were beating the Japanese at sea. It was officially announced that the V.2s were targeted on London. Nothing like them had been seen in the world before. Going up to 30 miles above the earth, they were faster than sound, able to penetrate the deepest shelter and gave no warning of approach - they were very frightening.

My mother and I left Sturton and went up to London with camp beds to look at No. 12 for two nights. While we were there, two landed fairly near, and another in the distance. The strange thing was to hear them coming after they had landed and exploded.

No. 12 was in a grim state of delapidation. Its emptiness was accentuated by scattered dust and minor rubble. I tried in vain to clear a clean space to set up our beds. The task seemed overwhelming. We arrived back at Sturton cold and dirty. Violet said, "Thank goodness you're back, it's been awfully spooky."

Violet had another dreadful postcard:

IMPERIAL JAPANESE ARMY
Date 10-1-44

YOUR MAILS (AND   ) ARE RECEIVED (WITH THANKS)

MY HEALTH IS (GOOD, USUAL, POOR)

I am ill in Hospital

I am working for pay (I am paid a monthly salary)

I am not working

My best regards to Everyone

Yours ever

David Brocus

'Your mails are received with thanks' was crossed out, and so was 'I am ill in hospital' and 'I am paid a monthly salary'. The only bit in David's handwriting was 'Everyone' and his name.

My Diary, 23rd December:
The Germans have counter-attacked in Belgium, in the Ardennes. The Americans have been cut off. Supposing that we are driven back into the sea again and have another Dunkirk, and then some dreadful new weapon is unleashed against us - a weapon so terrible that retaliation is impossible and after all these years we lose the war.

1944:
My mother came into the kitchen and said, "Happy Christmas, Violet!"
Violet pulled a wry face.
"Alright, have it your own way," my mother moaned.
Ann is the only cheerful one - she has been so occupied arranging Christmas for the men in the Convalescent Home that she hadn't the time to mope.
The Aunts sent Johnie presents. I've made Daisy a woolly rabbit out of unravelled jersey - made up of rainbow colours - but he lacks whiskers.

New Year 1945:

I remember thinking, 'These are the years that the locusts have eaten'. I doubted if they could ever be restored as the Bible promised. Often I thought about Andrew and wondered how he could possibly manage just to abandon Violet; and then again, I imagined that he found the situation so unbearable that he decided to suffer in the wilderness for her sake.

Johnie was tall for his age, pale and silent, but Daisy, born out of anguish, was boisterous and happy. The sound of the locusts grinding away at our lives obviously never touched her. She hardly ever cried and her joyous shouts echoed through the moods and rooms of Chapel House. We soon gave up calling her Daisy. She became known as 'the Bouncing Bomb' and then as 'Bomber' - Violet said, "I really hate you calling Daisy 'Bomber'. I do wish you wouldn't." But the name stuck.

My Diary, 15th February:
The city of Dresden has been bombed. A fire-storm followed the high explosives.

18th February:
The RAF have tried to put the launching sites of the V.2.s out of action, or to harass them continually so that they have to move them back out of range.

9th March:
Tokyo raided heavily.

18th March:
V.2 rockets smashing down on London again. Daisy's birthday.

27th April:
Russians and Americans coming from east and west have met on the River Elbe.

30th April:

The Russians are in Berlin. Hitler has killed himself and Eva Braun in his bunker. Faithful followers have destroyed the bodies by fire - there is nothing left of them.

8th May:

The war is over - at least in Europe. There are great celebrations in London and elsewhere. Nothing is happening here at Sturton, of course. Johnie and I went and sat under the apple tree. I carried Bomber - Bristles followed us. "This is a very important day," I told Johnie. "The war has come to an end, but not all of it." I had to explain that the Japanese part was still going on.

Johnie said, "I want to join in."

CHAPTER 60

The day after V.E. day, I went into my mother's room. Bristles was on her lap. We talked about David - although the Japanese were being forced back everywhere and slowly being driven out of the Pacific Islands one by one, we came to the desperate conclusion that this might go on for years and years, and when at last they were beaten, it was very unlikely that many prisoners would be left alive - any remaining in captivity would probably be executed. We both cried while the V.E. celebrations went on.

"We shall have to pray for a miracle," my mother said. "A miracle that somehow something happens to release them and set them free."

Eight days later Ian turned up. He was flown out of Germany from Munich by the Americans to somewhere in France and thence to England.

We were at supper when we heard the front door - it was Ian. He called out, "Ann,". She jumped up from the table and ran. In her haste she tripped on the carpet, but he caught her before she fell.

Mother and I both agreed that Ian's homecoming mustn't be spoilt because of David.

The terrible miracle happened on the 20th July.

It wasn't until 16th October that David arrived back. He had been flown from Thailand to Rangoon, and travelled home by boat. He was unbelievably thin and ill.

What happened between him and Violet, we never knew, but one thing was obvious - he seemed to think it was all my mother's fault. His coldness towards her remained always.

My mother and I stayed at Chapel House for a month after David's return and then we moved back to London - leaving them there alone.

It was a whole year before David's health showed much sign of improvement. His feet were always shockingly painful, because they had been broken with stones by the Japanese guards.

His eyesight too had suffered. His recovery was painfully slow.

For me, parting with Johnie was hard.

Bristles was glad to be back in London. He never had cared much for the country and was always nervous of the birds, and the criminal cat next door.

It's a long time since the war ended - fifty years ago. People who were old then are mostly gone and those who are young have become old.

Living as I do now, far removed and distant from my past life, I suddenly had a longing to write down the story of our family in crisis during the war. Events were brought to life by the scribbles in my diary and my memories are very vivid. It has been a nostalgic task - full of sadness and, strangely enough, homesickness.

David was unable to continue serving in the Army, partly because of his health and partly because his career had been so damaged by being out of action in captivity for so long. - As the saying goes 'There is no promotion in the bag', so it seemed unwise for him to continue to struggle against such odds. In the end he went back to Cambridge and studied Law. He and Violet had one more child - a boy. They called him William - after all, David was the beloved of our father.

Ian went on flying for some time, and then he and Ann took over the running of her stepfather's estate which they later inherited. They had four daughters.

My mother sold Chapel House and also sold No. 12, and bought a cottage near Marchfold, which she shared with May, who was by that time widowed - not by death, but by a secretary.

Johnie is a soldier.

Violet's brother, Stephen, became a missionary in Central Africa.

I have lost touch with the cousins; chiefly, I suppose, because of my Indian connection.

I have one daughter called Bassanti, after the flower that grows in the Himalayas, imported into English gardens - it is known as 'winter jasmine'.

Hannah Rawat
New Delhi 1993

254